FINDING BALANCE
IN A MEDICAL LIFE

Finding Balance in a Medical Life

RECLAIMING YOUR LIFE WHILE SERVING OTHERS

Lee Lipsenthal, MD

Finding Balance, Inc.
San Anselmo, California

Finding Balance in a Medical Life
First Edition

Text design by R. C. Diebold, www.LeftCoastGraphics.com

Cover design by Natalie Cedarquist

First printing, August 2007

ISBN-0-9785321-1-2

Printed in United States of America

Distributed by Finding Balance, Inc.

Finding Balance, Inc.
106 Spring Grove Ave
San Anselmo, California 94960

Dedication

This book is dedicated to the following individuals:

Jim Billings, in the truest meaning of the word, my mentor and friend.
I learned a lifetime of wisdom from you in ten years of lunches together.

Dean Ornish, who taught me how to manifest.

Nita Gage, who held my hand as I grew.

My colleagues and friends who make this life fun and exciting — the ABHM
Board of Directors, my 'partner in crime' Larry Cooper, The whole PMRI
gang, Glenn and Ronna Perelson, Melanie Elliot and Michael Eller, Sandy
Aquila, Bertrand Vandeville, Larry Harrison and Karen Knighton, Vivian
Baron, Anna and Mark Silberman, Rikki and Bronwyn Cooke, Mike and Saori
Kappus, Mimi Guarneri and Rauni Pritkin-King, Ben Brown, Denny Malone,
Benji Schiano, Pam and Bart Wald, Steve McDermott, Peter Lee, Walt Mills,
Frank Harris, Amy, John, and Tiny.

The HeartMath Team for their clarity, generosity and support.

The physicians of the world who are working to make our lives better.

The many musicians of the world who provide joy.

The many great teachers from whom I have learned (mentioned in this book).

Those angels who somehow know when to show up when I need them most
— Jim Levine, Natalie Cederquist, and Randy Perkins.

My parents, who showed me what love looked like as they danced together
when they thought we weren't watching.

Kathy, who instilled me with a desire to learn how to love well.

Will and Cheryl, who taught me how to love unconditionally.

Contents

Opening Remarks...i

Forward...iii

Introduction 1

Chapter 1 **Balance** 7

Chapter 2 **Are We Happy?**...13

Chapter 3 **How Did We Get to This Place?**.....................................23

Chapter 4 **The Physician Personality**...29

Chapter 5 **Our Health** 59

Chapter 6 **Stress and Burnout** 63

Chapter 7 **The Road Within**...69

Chapter 8 **What Makes a Happy Doc Happy?** 73

Chapter 9 **Managing Stress**...79

Chapter 10 **A Cognitive Approach to Perspective Shifting** 81

Chapter 11 **Emotional Shifting and Emotional Intelligence**....................89

Chapter 12 **Connection**...97

Chapter 13 **Connection and Communication** 107

Chapter 14 **Meditation**..113

Chapter 15 **Psychosynthesis**...127

Chapter 16 **Moving Forward** 149

Chapter 17 **What Is Balance?**..155

Notes 155

Bibliography 169

Suggested Reading..183

About the Author 187

Opening Remarks

A few years ago I was treated by a physician in his late forties whom I had known for some years. He was widely respected and highly dedicated to his patients. But he looked terrible: overweight, tired, and pallid. I told him so. His "doctor" image deflated as he visibly sagged. He mentioned some pressures: a malpractice case, some problems in his office, the daily race to keep up. He said he just had to get through the next few months and he would be fine. Instead, he died of a massive heart attack within the year, leaving behind a beautiful family.

This is an extreme but not isolated story. I work with hundreds of physicians in my role as CEO of Hill Physicians Medical Group.* I see too many symptoms of burnout. It was serendipity that I happened to meet Lee Lipsenthal, MD, one Sunday afternoon in Berkeley (of course), where he was teaching a course with Dean Ornish, MD. It was this chance interaction that ultimately led to Lee's presenting his Finding Balance in a Medical Life program at Hill. The initial reaction by our physician leadership was dubious; however, now four years later, the quarterly program is consistently sold out. And, at the request of physician participants, a parallel program has been developed for practice staff with similar rave reviews.

The medical profession is unique, particularly as practiced in the United States, with the extraordinary challenges and demands made upon its members. I sometimes refer to this as "John Wayne medicine," but Jimmy Stewart in *High Noon* is probably more accurate: the lone stalwart sheriff going up against the seemingly unstoppable bad guys. If we get it right in reorganizing health care to become a team effort, maybe in another generation we won't tax our practitioners as we have. But for now, Lee's book provides just what the doctor ordered.

Steve McDermott
Chief Executive Officer
Hill Physicians Medical Group

---

*An Independent Practice Association in Northern California composed of 2,600 physicians with 350,000 HMO patients.

Forward

Most physicians went into medicine because they wanted to lead a life of service and make a meaningful difference in the lives of their patients. They worked hard just to get into medical school; worked hard to complete medical school, internship, residency, and fellowship; and continue to work hard to keep up with the demands of practice and research.

After years of training and hard work, they often find themselves squeezed — forced by managed care to see more patients in less time for less money, and to spend long hours arguing with insurance companies about coverage for appropriate treatments. The physician can start to feel besieged on all sides.

Perhaps then it's not surprising that in a survey of 1,300 physicians nationwide, 63 percent replied that they wouldn't recommend medicine as a career to their children , or that physicians die younger than those in other professions and have among the highest rates of addiction and suicide.

It doesn't have to be this way. Awareness is the first step in healing, and suffering can be a powerful catalyst for personal transformation. *Finding Balance in a Medical Life* by Lee Lipsenthal, MD, is an eloquent, potent way of enhancing awareness and promoting healing in ourselves, our families, and our patients.

I began working with Lee more than twenty years ago when he was medical director of the nonprofit Preventive Medicine Research Institute that I founded. Together, we conducted a series of research and demonstration projects showing that comprehensive lifestyle changes may begin to reverse the progression of coronary heart disease, prostate cancer, diabetes, hypertension, obesity, hypercholesterolemia, and other chronic diseases. We used high-tech, expensive, state-of-the-art medical technology to prove the power of low-tech, inexpensive, and, often, ancient interventions.

The insights we gained from this clinical experience, as well as the extraordinary work that Lee has gone on to do since then, form the basis of this remarkable book. Lee is a doctor's doctor who embodies the best qualities of a physician — keen intellect, excellent clinician, compassionate friend, and clear communicator.

Finding Balance in a Medical Life is a call to action that may help you save a very important life — yours.

Dean Ornish, MD
Founder and President, Preventive Medicine Research Institute
Clinical Professor of Medicine, University of California, San Francisco

Introduction

Our lives as physicians are filled with blessings. We are with people in birth, death, and illness. We are honored to enter their lives in their most vulnerable moments and to share the joys of their lives with them. For most of us, this feels like a true mission, yet the busyness of our lives leads us to a state of fatigue, exhaustion, and even burnout. How can we reclaim our lives, our missions, and passions, while gaining greater self-awareness and love in our lives? I hope you will find the answer through the tools and concepts I present in this book.

My own story in medicine is rather ordinary. I was raised in an upper-middle–class suburb of New York City. I came from a family and town where having a professional career was a common expectation. Being a doctor meant being "somebody." I had the opportunity to know many fine physicians who were role models. One such man was our family doctor and friend, Mort Cassel. He was a caring, soft-spoken man who would make house calls when we were ill and invariably make us feel better, often with his presence alone. He inspired me to consider medicine as a career. The other role model was my father, a dedicated and caring family dentist.

I went to an East Coast college where I was surrounded by pre-med and pre-law students. In this atmosphere, going into medicine seemed like the right and admirable thing to do. My grade-point average, however, was not stellar. My first year of applying to medical school consisted of over fifty applications and just as many rejection letters.

I began to "tune myself up." I exercised one and a half to two hours each day (to the point of obsession). I put myself on a rigid diet (I was a chubby teen). I enrolled in a one-year masters program in human physiology and earned a 4.0 average. In essence, I used all of my type-A behaviors to their fullest. What did this get me? Fifty more rejection letters.

I needed to find work that would enhance my chances of getting into medical school and provide a backup career if I didn't get in. I had already worked in hospitals during college, so I didn't feel that was the key. Instead, I decided to work in a science lab, as I loved neurophysiology (yes, I can be a quite the nerd). I set about applying for any lab job in neurology that I could find and was lucky to land a job working with a great neuro-anatomy teacher, and later friend, Sal Rapisardi, at Howard University.

This was a great year of learning science, studying, and learning how to write scientific papers. I became part of the affiliate teaching staff and got to know the faculty quite well. I still kept the applications flowing and continued to get rejection letters. My desire to become a physician was fueled by the rejection, so I began to apply to medical schools in other countries. In my third year of applications I was accepted to a medical school in northern France. I was excited and extremely anxious about moving to an unfamiliar country. I began to get rid of possessions, decide what I could bring with me, and adjust to the fact that I would be far from my family and friends for many years.

Two weeks before leaving, I received a call from the dean's office of Howard University telling me that I had cleared the waiting list and was accepted into Howard's medical school. I still don't know who, if anyone I knew, pulled the strings, but after three years and over a hundred applications, I was in!

In medical school, academically, I shined. In my three years of applications to school, I learned self-discipline — how to eat, exercise, and study — all of which served me well in the rigors of medical education. During medical school, I began a self-taught practice of meditation from reading books and listening to cassette tapes of meditation teachers. I found this to be particularly useful around exam time, as meditation gave me a greater sense of clarity and calm going into exams. The learning process became fun and the challenge was like training for a marathon. I didn't know it then, but the meditation practice I had started would become the door that opened up new awareness and opportunities for me later in my career.

As any athlete knows, training takes coaching. Some of my medical school faculty served this role. One, whom I will always remember, was Dr. Lasalle LaFall. He was loved by his patients, students, and fellow faculty members. He was politically and scientifically active in his field of medicine. As a teacher, he was without equal. He was there for us as students and as individuals. Even today his wise advice resonates in my head: "At the end of each day, ask yourself if there is anything you did today that you can do better tomorrow." He also appeared tireless and unflappable. He was in the hospital before us (about 6:00 AM) and often left after us (around 8:00 PM). He had incredible integrity, honesty, and sincere empathy at all hours. He was truly what I wanted to be when I completed my training.

Now more than twenty years later, I look back at that wonderful man and know that, had I become him, I probably would not have the marriage that I have and would not know my children as I know them today. I wouldn't have been home to see my children's first steps or hear their first words; Kathy and I would not have spent the hours we have in building and growing our relationship.

I certainly don't wish to diminish this great man's life or influence on all of my classmates, but today, I prefer not to be him. I prefer not to work tirelessly in medicine. I prefer to enjoy my career and my family. What made me change my mind about who I wanted to be?

The process of change began for me after my residency, after falling in love, after having two children. The wake-up call occurred while riding the trolley to my office in Philadelphia. I was struck with a near panic attack. I was three years out of residency, working in a downtown, corporate, mainstream, suit-and-tie office practice. As an internist with a strong interest in lipids and cardiovascular prevention, I spent most of my day seeing individuals who were interested in decreasing their risk of heart attack and stroke. A noble calling, but on that particular morning the thought of hearing myself say, "low-fat diet, exercise, manage stress, take your medications," twenty to thirty times over the next few hours became unbearable. The routine of medicine and the repetition of my own words were driving me crazy.

Those outside the medical field believe that the stress in medicine comes from dramatic events such as the ones they see on TV. For most physicians, that level of excitement and challenge is fun. What is more stressful for clinicians are the routine, mundane, day-to-day occurrences like paperwork, phone calls, dictating or typing charts, and repeating the same information over and over to people who may only be half-listening or half-understanding. The routine was killing me; I was hungry for drama or challenge.

It was at this moment that I realized that the way I was practicing medicine wasn't working for me. At that time, Kathy (my wife and also an internist) and I had two children, two jobs, and too much in our lives. I, by all external standards, was a success, and yet I was in a state of panic and depression from being simultaneously overworked and bored to tears!

I didn't think medicine was supposed to be boring or routine. "It wasn't supposed to be like this!" I was burning up my energy whining about what the practice of medicine was supposed to be like, and not enjoying what it really was like. What I was yet to learn was that my *perceptions* were at the root of my anxieties.

This lesson would come to me through studying meditation, Eastern philosophy, emotional intelligence, and neurophysiology: "Before enlightenment, chop wood, carry water. After enlightenment, chop wood, carry water." I needed to learn how to live within my routine with clarity and happiness, and understand that out of this comes authenticity and performance. I realized that the challenge was not learning how to be a great doctor, but learning how to live a great life while using my medical skills and knowledge.

Along this incredible journey, I have helped to run a large downtown medical office and cardiac rehabilitation center, as well as a research institute, and have taught and learned from physicians worldwide about medicine and our lives as practitioners. I have meditated, studied spirituality, neurophysiology, shamanism, integrative or holistic medicine, organizational development, and psychology. This book is the result of that journey.

I want to share the process of self-analysis and self-awareness that has helped me achieve my goals. It is about remembering to have a life! It is about the current state of medicine and how we got here. It is about who we are as physicians and how this works for us and against us. It is about unwinding this puzzle and learning to be happier and healthier. We can be better family members, community leaders, and teachers to our patients.

This book will help you gain clarity, flexibility, and life balance. The tools and concepts in this book come not from me but from worldwide-respected, ancient philosophies exploring the human spirit, soul, and psyche. These tools have been applied by spiritual teachers, psychologists, and business consultants for many years with the goal of transforming individual's lives and the way groups of people function together. In essence, I've created nothing new; I have brought together tools and practices that I've found most useful and consolidated them into a simple format to help you move forward in your life with greater clarity and purpose. This is a tool kit for your own process of growth, change, and potential to thrive in your career. This book will plant the seeds of future personal growth, shift your perspectives, enhance your flexibility, improve your productivity, and increase pleasure in your life. I hope it serves you well.

By choosing to read this book, you have realized, to some extent, that your life in the realm of medicine and health care is not balanced. It may be far out of whack or just in need of fine tuning. Personally, I have felt the stress of medicine, have experienced burnout, and also at times, just need minor adjustments in attitude.

The structure of this book is simple. You will enjoy it and learn by reading small bits at a time or by reading it in its complete form. The first few chapters are about how we have come to this place of high stress in medicine. The later chapters, beginning with chapter 7, "The Road Within," are a collection of tools that I have gathered and refined over my years of questing balance. I now will hand this tool kit over to you. I encourage you to use it as a resource for personal growth.

The best way to use the tool kit is to try out each tool for a week or so, understand its effectiveness, and then bring it out when you need it later. These tools also build on each other, so they are best learned in sequence.

Some tools will be *maintenance tools;* these prevent problems from occurring. Other tools are *restructuring tools;* these will help rebuild your house or add additions. And then there are the *crisis tools;* these will help you to manage events as they arise.

Additional tools and fun toys can be found on my web site: www.findingbalanceproductions.com.

Please remember, tools only work when you use them. They are of no purpose sitting in the garage!

The Real Deal

There is nothing more potent or life changing than love and gratitude. I learned this by witnessing my family, meditating, reading, and listening. If this book reminds of nothing more than that, I have done my job well.

CHAPTER 1

Balance

Imagine life as a game in which you are juggling five balls in the air. You name them — work, family, health, friends, and spirit — and you're keeping all of these in the air. You will soon understand that work is a rubber ball. If you drop it, it will bounce back. But the other four balls — family, health, friends, and spirit — are made of glass. If you drop one of these, they will be irrevocably scuffed, marked, nicked, damaged, or even shattered. They will never be the same. You must understand that and strive for balance in your life.

— Brian Dyson, CEO of Coca Cola Enterprises from 1959–1994

Life balance is often talked about, but not often achieved on a day-to-day basis. Most of us have days in which we feel balanced, rested, and passionate, only to be followed by days or moments of anger, frustration, or fatigue. I therefore think of balance as the stability to ride the winds of change. To be successful and happy, one must be ready to catch the wind when it arises.

In order to catch and use the winds of change, your ship should be well tended, your sails well mended, your maps and charts in order, and your mind well intended. Your maps, sails, ship, and charts can be viewed as major themes in your life. If these things are in order, you will be shipshape and can ride the winds of life with full pleasure while traversing the greatest of oceans. Our charts, sails, intentions, and captain are as follows.

Your Physical Health
The basic body needs must be met. This includes food, water, and sleep. The first two, we physicians do well with; it is the latter where we are deficient. Physical health also includes exercise. I will not go into details on diet and exercise, as our literature base is filled with good information in these areas. Keep in mind, however, that your physical well-being affects your emotional and mental well-being. Also, remember that dead doctors serve no one. Physical health cannot be put off, but for many of us, we need to get our emotional health together first. I recommend that you do these things simultaneously.

Emotional Well-Being
This includes pleasures, love, and joy as well as learning to manage uncomfortable or undesirable emotions. This book will emphasize this area by guiding you through the emotional complexities of medicine as well as our own personalities. It will also show you the power of relationships to transform a meaningless life into a life with purpose.

Spiritual Well-Being
Spirituality can be defined in many ways that incorporate religious practices

and beliefs or can be of a non-religious nature. I leave this up to you; however, spirituality generally includes a sense of connection with others and a sense of connection with something larger than us. Our health is strongly linked to this state of being.

Mental Well-Being

Mental well-being includes the processes of learning, creating, and experiencing personal growth. It also includes the concept of emotional intelligence, the idea that emotions affect your functionality, performance, and outcomes.

The type-A approach to these life components would be, "I'll exercise one hour daily, then I will tell all my friends and family that I love them. Maybe I can call my friends and family when I am on the treadmill working out. Then I will pray for thirty minutes, meditate for twenty, and then read the literature for an hour." How many of you can add three hours to your day and still get enough sleep?

The goal is to be aware of these life components and keep them alive in your day. There may be times, for example, studying for a board exam, when you won't get enough exercise or downtime; but when the exam is over, try to reestablish your routine. Most importantly, be gentle with yourself. Allow yourself to be perfectly imperfect.

I encourage you, upon waking each morning, to ask yourself which of the four components needs your attention today. Then, make the time to attend to that need that day. With this, over time, balance can be achieved.

Internal Balance Assessment

Let's start to evaluate your state of balance by using the Holistic Health Assessment, designed for patients by The American Board of Holistic Medicine (see www.holisticboard.org).

Answer the questions in each section below and total your score. Answer the questions honestly. This is for self-assessment purposes. Each response will be a number from 0 to 5. Please refer to the frequency described within the parentheses (e.g., 2–3 times per week) when answering questions about an *activity*, for example, "Do you maintain a healthy diet?" However, when the question refers to an *attitude* or an *emotion* (most of the Mind and Spirit questions), for example, "Do you have a sense of humor?" the response is more subjective, less exact, and you can refer only to the items describing the frequency, such as *often* or *daily*, but not to the numbered frequencies in parentheses.

0 = Never or almost never (once a year or less)
1 = Seldom (2–12 times per year)
2 = Occasionally (2–4 times per month)
3 = Often (2–3 times per week)
4 = Regularly (4–6 times per week)
5 = Daily (every day)

Body: Physical and Environmental Health

_____ 1. Do you maintain a healthy diet (low fat, low sugar, fresh fruits, grains, and vegetables)?

_____ 2. Is your water intake adequate (at least _ oz./lb. of body weight; 160 lbs. = 80 oz.)?

_____ 3. Are you within 20 percent of your ideal body weight?

_____ 4. Do you feel physically attractive?

_____ 5. Do you fall asleep easily and sleep soundly?

_____ 6. Do you awaken in the morning feeling well rested?

_____ 7. Do you have more than enough energy to meet your daily responsibilities?

_____ 8. Are your five senses acute?

_____ 9. Do you take time to experience sensual pleasure?

_____ 10. Do you schedule regular massage or deep-tissue bodywork?

_____ 11. Does your sexual relationship feel gratifying?

_____ 12. Do you engage in regular physical workouts lasting at least twenty minutes?

_____ 13. Do you have good endurance or aerobic capacity?

_____ 14. Do you breathe abdominally for at least a few minutes?

_____ 15. Do you maintain physically challenging goals?

_____ 16. Are you physically strong?

_____ 17. Do you do some stretching exercises?

_____ 18. Are you free of chronic aches, pains, ailments, and diseases?

_____ 19. Do you have regular effortless bowel movements?

_____ 20. Do you understand the causes of your chronic physical problems?

_____ 21. Are you free of any drug or alcohol dependency (including nicotine and caffeine)?

_____ 22. Do you live in a healthy environment with respect to clean air, water, and indoor pollution?

_____ 23. Do you feel energized or empowered by nature?

_____ 24. Do you feel a strong connection with and appreciation for your body, your home, and your environment?

_____ 25. Do you have an awareness of life energy, or qi (from Asian medicine)?

Total Body Score _____

Mind: Mental and Emotional Health

_____ 1. Do you have specific goals in your personal and professional life?

_____ 2. Do you have the ability to concentrate for extended periods of time?

_____ 3. Do you use visualization or mental imagery to help you attain your goals or enhance your performance?

_____ 4. Do you believe it is possible to change?

_____ 5. Can you meet your financial needs and desires?

_____ 6.   Is your outlook basically optimistic?

_____ 7. Do you give yourself more supportive messages than critical messages?

_____ 8. Does your job use all of your greatest talents?

_____ 9. Is your job enjoyable and fulfilling?

_____ 10. Are you willing to take risks or make mistakes in order to succeed?

_____ 11. Are you able to adjust beliefs and attitudes as a result of learning from painful experiences?

_____ 12. Do you have a sense of humor?

_____ 13. Do you maintain peace of mind and tranquility?

_____ 14. Are you free from a strong need for control or to be right?

_____ 15. Are you able to fully experience (feel) your painful feelings such as fear, anger, sadness, and hopelessness?

_____ 16. Are you aware of and able to safely express fear?

_____ 17. Are you aware of and able to safely express anger?

_____ 18. Are you aware of and able to safely express sadness or to cry?

_____ 19. Are you accepting of all of your feelings?

_____ 20. Do you engage in meditation, contemplation, or psychotherapy to better understand your feelings?

_____ 21. Is your sleep free from disturbing dreams?

_____ 22. Do you explore the symbolism and emotional content of your dreams?

_____ 23. Do you take the time to let down and relax, or make time for activities that constitute the abandon or absorption of play?

_____ 24. Do you experience feelings of exhilaration?

_____ 25. Do you enjoy high self-esteem?

Total Mind/Emotions Score _____

Spirit: Spiritual and Social Health

_____ 1. Do you actively commit time to your spiritual life?

_____ 2. Do you take time for prayer, meditation, or reflection?

_____ 3. Do you listen to your intuition?

_____ 4. Are creative activities a part of your work or leisure time?

_____ 5. Do you take risks or exceed previous limits?

_____ 6. Do you have faith in a god, spirit guides, or angels?

_____ 7. Are you free from anger toward God or your higher power?

_____ 8. Are you grateful for the blessings in your life?

_____ 9. Do you take walks, garden, or have contact with nature?

_____ 10. Are you able to let go of your attachment to specific outcomes and embrace uncertainty?

_____ 11. Do you observe a day of rest completely away from work, dedicated to nurturing yourself and your family?

_____ 12. Can you let go of self-interest in deciding the best course of action for a given situation?

_____ 13. Do you feel a sense of purpose?

_____ 14. Do you make time to connect with young children, either your own or someone else's?

_____ 15. Are playfulness and humor important to you in your daily life?

_____ 16. Do you have the ability to forgive yourself and others?

_____ 17. Have you demonstrated the willingness to commit to a marriage or compatible long-term relationship?

_____ 18. Do you experience intimacy, besides sex, in your committed relationships?

_____ 19. Do you confide in or speak openly with one or more close friends?

_____ 20. Do you or did you feel close to your parents?

_____ 21. If you have experienced the loss of a loved one, have you fully grieved that loss?

_____ 22. Has your experience of pain enabled you to grow spiritually?

_____ 23. Do you go out of your way or give time to help others?

_____ 24. Do you feel a sense of belonging to a group or community?

_____ 25. Do you experience unconditional love?

Total Spirit Score _____

Total Body, Mind, Spirit Score (add all categories) _____

Your Health Scale

325–375 Optimal Health

275–324 Excellent Health

225–274 Good Health

175 –224 Fair Health

125–174 Below-Average Health

75–124 Poor Health

0–74 Extremely Poor Health = Surviving

Based on the above assessment, what is the current state of your life balance today? Where can you use a little help? Admitting the need for help is the first step in the direction of change. This is true for any behavioral change model.

CHAPTER 2 **Are We Happy?**

Are the majority of physicians today enjoying their work? Multiple surveys have shown that physicians are increasingly dissatisfied with their practices and have trouble finding work-life balance.

In 2001 a Kaiser Family Foundation survey of 2,608 physicians showed that 60 percent of physicians had experienced a decrease in enthusiasm toward the practice of medicine. In the preceding five years, 87 percent said that the overall morale of physicians had declined in those years; and 75 percent said that managed care had had a negative impact on their practices. The survey further asked for reasons why the physicians were unhappy. Seventy-four percent of respondents cited excessive administrative duties as the reason; 56 percent said they did not have enough time for their families, hobbies, and friends; and 54 percent were dissatisfied with a lack of autonomy. (See KKF.org)

Looking at these data, who is responsible? Surely we are not passive participants in the medical system without intelligence and power to change! Or have we given up our power and autonomy to others and become the victims of a process that is spinning out of control. As you proceed through this book, you will look at how you have given up your personal power and how you can capture it again. You will also evaluate how much of these issues result from your own attitudes, how much are because of others, and how much you can change things.

These data on physician discontentment are not unusual. Multiple studies, over the last two decades, reflect increasing physician work dissatisfaction and high levels of burnout. In almost all studies, roughly one third of physicians state that they would not choose medicine as a career again, and approximately the same number are dissatisfied with their current choice of specialty.

If you are not already depressed about the state of medicine, dwelling on data like this will cause you to get there quickly. More importantly, getting depressed does not create the energy needed to facilitate change. Therefore, rather than dwell on all the depressing data, I'd like to focus on one study and use it to help us understand why we are unhappy and thus see what we can do about it.

In 1999, Erica Frank, MD, and colleagues published a comprehensive review of the work satisfaction of women physicians.[1] This study was unusual for two reasons: First, it focused on women physicians, a growing part of our medical base (by 2010, 30 percent of all practicing physicians will be women). Second, it looked at lifestyle issues in relation to career satisfaction. This makes it an important jumping-off point for discussion on enhancing our own life balance.

13

In this study, 4,501 women physicians were surveyed from the AMA master file of practicing physicians. Three key questions were asked: (1) "Are you generally satisfied with your career?" (2) "If you relived your life, would you still want to become a physician?" and (3) "Would you change your specialty?"

The key outcomes were as follows: Eighty-four percent of those surveyed were always, almost always, or usually satisfied with their careers; 69 percent would choose to be a physician again; and 62 percent would probably want to stay in their specialty. This is good news; however, the pessimist in me says that this also means that 31 percent would not choose medicine again and that 38 percent are unsatisfied in their specialties.

Let's look at the variants involved and their relationships to satisfaction at work.

Age
In this study, the younger physicians (under age forty) were less happy than the older ones, yet the younger physicians were happier in their specialties. There are many issues involved with this outcome. Older women physicians entered medicine at a time when career choices were limited; therefore it makes sense that they would be less happy in their specialties today. They had to exceed expectations just to be seen as professionals by their male colleagues and teachers. Older women physicians are more likely to have balance in their home lives and to have older children. In essence their lives today are under greater control. This gives a greater sense of stability and lower amounts of home stress. Home stress, as I will discuss later, is a major contributor to work stress.

Younger women physicians have greater career choices and are therefore more likely to be happy in their specialty; however, the young woman physician today is filling multiple roles and has much less financial stability than her older colleagues. There are also societal issues at play here. The majority of women physicians have spouses who are working full-time. This means that there is no one taking care of the home, which has traditionally in our society been the role of the woman. This is a great stress for most women; therefore, their overall life stress is higher.

If the younger female physician can gain, through personal exploration, the wisdom usually acquired through aging, then stability and satisfaction can emerge while in a specialty she enjoys. For the male reader, there is an edge here: the older male doctor had greater career choices from the beginning.

Children, Families and Multiple Roles
Dr. Frank and colleagues also found that physicians who had multiple life roles were happier in their careers. This is a substantial finding. Many people believe that the more children you have, the more stress you have. This is often mentioned at the coffee shop in between "chauffeur" jobs to soccer practice, play practice, and the multitude of things our children practice. This study suggests that this belief is not true.

There are probably many reasons that physicians with more children are happier. For example, the activities above would distract physicians from thinking about medicine and therefore prevent them from perseverating about their patients or problems in their practice. This gives your brain a break by taking your focus off work. Children's activities and needs also provide a reason to get out of work and away from the practice more frequently. I believe that, in most work environments, children are the most socially acceptable excuse to leave work early. Young and single physicians tend to stay later and work more hours. This is often because they are insecure, energetic, and don't have a reason to escape, such as children. Although it has not been measured as such, in medicine, I also believe that physicians with young children at home are forced to become more efficient, take on fewer meaningless tasks, and limit their obligations, thus enhancing their sense of balance.

Children also keep us in-line. It's difficult to play the decisive, egocentric doctor with your child. They set you straight! This will be a very important aspect to remember in this book's section on sub-personalities and psychosynthesis (see chapter 15). We adopt a very different set of behaviors with our children than with our patients; we are a different personality in many ways.

For me, one of the greatest lessons from my children was letting go of control. My life prior to the birth of our children had been about me, even after I was married. At first, my life was about music, play, exercise, and school; all of which were my choices and within my control. After marriage, as two medical students, our focus was on our careers and relationship. The arrival of our children turned these notions upside down. We had to focus on our careers, but we now had to become life partners, not just lovers and best friends.

Many years later, I was struck with the change in my perspective. On a conference call, a friend of mine, a bright, aggressive woman in business, talked about what her life would be like after giving birth. Her statement about her unborn child was, "She'll adjust to my schedule." At that moment, we muted the phone, and those of us with children started to crack up in laughter. Any of you with children know the insanity of a statement like that, but try to explain that to someone who is eight months pregnant and strong willed. Having a baby turns your life upside down. Personally, with our first child, I struggled with my need for control, but the love of a little girl helped me surpass that need. As I am a slow learner, that lesson was reinforced with the birth of our son. I had to accept that it was no longer my life, it was our life. Thank you, Cheryl and Will, for that lesson.

Children provide us with community. For those readers with children, you know that many of your friends are the parents of your children's classmates and playmates. You learn to depend on each other for carpooling, and you spend time together at your children's events. Soon many of these people become your best friends. It may take a community to raise a child, but it takes a child to raise a parent.

More importantly children teach us how to love: when you hold your baby, when you fall asleep reading to your seven-year-old, when you and your spouse watch your child play or graduate high school, you don't need to work to connect with heartfelt emotions. This happens easily and naturally. Just bear in mind what your children look like when they are asleep. For those of you with pets, picture them sleeping. I believe that we learn how to love unconditionally from our children, not necessarily from our spousal relationships. In the section on HeartMath (see chapter 11), I will discuss how this emotional connection makes us happier, healthier, and more emotionally intelligent.

Religiosity and Spirituality
Physicians who have a regular religious practice are happier in medicine. This sense of connection with community and with a greater purpose helps the physician stay in touch with the motivation of doing good for others, which is one of medicine's core values. Regardless of what religion or spiritual path you choose, participation keeps you in touch with this important value. Religion also provides us with a community and, more importantly, a community outside of medicine. One word of caution here, don't act like a doctor in your religious community; don't try to be in charge of everything. Don't become the president of your church or synagogue. You have enough responsibility in your life already. It doesn't matter if you can do the job, just say no. Just enjoy the sense of belonging. Enjoy being "Joe Average." I will show you in later chapters how this sense of connection motivates, energizes, and focuses the work of medicine and how taking on too much responsibility can diminish that effect.

Mental Health
Depression and anxiety contribute to workplace dissatisfaction. They also contribute to poor working relationships. Many of you might respond to this by saying, "If it weren't for _____ (fill in your nemesis du jour), I wouldn't be so depressed or anxious." While certain external circumstances can be, without doubt, quite noxious and trigger depression and anxiety, I will show you ways of managing them. Keep in mind that noxious events (and sweet ones too) are a part of life. You cannot control all of them. What you can control is your response to these events and therefore the effect they have on your life.

Specialty Choices and Work Environments
In the study cited above, physicians in specialties with "controllable lifestyles" (anesthesiology, dermatology, psychiatry, and pathology) were happier than those physicians in primary-care practices. Although radiology would usually be put on the list of controllable lifestyle specialties, radiologists were not as happy as others with controllable lifestyles.

In general, physicians have a high need for control. It makes sense that when physicians are in control of their time, they are more content. Controlling physician work hours is often difficult. In primary-care roles, one can limit one's hours by choosing a certain work environment, such as a clinic. Such a choice is not easy, in that it often means reduced income; but again, this is an area where there is some control.

Another aspect of the work-hours issue is the predictability of the hours. Physicians who stay later on nearly a daily basis are very discontented. Those who leave early are very happy. Interestingly, this has nothing to do with actual number of hours worked. The contentment or discontentment is more related to your expectations of your work. If they are met, you are happy. If the expectations are unmet, you are miserable. Looking at your career, do you tend to whine about always leaving late? If so, and if this has been a trend, it should be obvious that your job takes more hours than you would like. The answer to this problem is to change your job or your expectations, whichever seems easier.

If you choose a practice environment or job because it gives you less control, but greater income or benefits, keep in mind that it's your choice! We all have patients who take on the sick role for secondary gain. Many of us take on the victim role for the same reason. It gets us attention, it binds us together against a common enemy (usually HMOs, IPAs, or administrators), and it gives us a reason not to spend the energy to make necessary but difficult changes. The changes you need to make may be large, but being in the role of victim will not change a thing. It only perpetuates frustration, drains energy, and keeps you trapped. Get over it! Playing the victim never gives anyone energy or joy. If you are unhappy about your work scenario, first stop thinking of yourself as a victim; you had a hand in creating the environment.

> *As long as you can find someone else to blame for anything you are doing, you cannot be held accountable or responsible for your growth or the lack of it.*
>
> — Sun Bear
>
> Founder and Medicine Chief
> Bear Tribe Medicine Society

The Academic Life

In this study,1 physicians in academic environments were happier than those who were not. This is related directly to one of the main reasons we choose medicine as a career — we like science. This is one of our main drivers that we often don't attend to. Do you have a pile of journals at your bedside or desk side? Do you feel guilty that you haven't read them?

A close friend of mine told me about a scenario that occurred after the death of his father, a prominent psychiatrist. When my friend and his family were cleaning out his father's house, they found journals scattered all over. They could not believe the number of journals that his father had kept (read or unread). On the second day of cleaning, they found a walk-in closet that contained thousands of journals, some of them never opened. Ah, the power of obsession!

We all hold the belief, to some degree, that in one of these journals lies some wondrous pearl of wisdom that will make us a better doctor or help solve a patient's problem in the future. My question to you is, How will you find that pearl of wisdom in the mess next to your desk in anything less than twelve hours?

In the 1940s there were three major medical journals in the United States: all three were monthly subscriptions, two of which were newsletters. Keeping up with the literature meant pouring yourself a coffee on a Sunday, sitting in your comfy chair, and reading for an hour. Since that time, the volume of medical literature has grown exponentially. More research is being done worldwide, and it is more accessible than in the past. In addition, the average physician receives multiple journals, including throwaway journals, weekly. It is impossible to keep up with the literature anymore, yet when we see the overwhelming pile next to the bed, we feel incompetent as physicians and scientists. After all, we were told, "If you don't keep up with the literature, you are not enough". One colleague of mine was told, "If you don't keep up with the literature, people will die." What a ridiculous guilt trip. This creates anxiety and frustration for us all. It hits one of our shared personality traits smack in the face — perfectionism! I will address this in the next chapter.

There is an old joke: "Why is North America sinking at a rate of 2 mm per year? It's because of the weight of all the *National Geographic* magazines that no one throws out." In our two-physician household, it's the weight of all the journals we subscribe to along with all the throwaways we receive. We have earthquake insurance, but living on a California hillside, we should be more concerned about sliding down the hill from information overload. Medicine is truly a weighty subject!

When I was at National Institutes of Health (NIH), I was in love with the National Library of Medicine. I would call in advance and describe to the librarian (a true library scientist) what I needed and would show up a few hours later to go through what had been found. If I needed more, the librarian would search for me and offer me coffee. This was academic-nerd heaven! Today we all have such a resource: it's called the Internet. It is possible to download and store all the information you need on your hard drive or a disc, but you have to get your own coffee.

A key message here is this: Let go of the old paradigm of keeping up with the literature, and be thankful that you have a world of information at your fingertips. Take an hour a week to read a journal or two. Enjoy what you can read, and know that it serves your patient, quells your anxieties, and feeds you inner science nerd, an important part of who we are as physicians. Be thankful that the Internet is at your finger tips. It is now feasible to search the literature for answers within seconds.

Long Hours

Working uncertain hours is part of the profession. We knew this when we went into medicine. People get sick at 3:00 AM. We can have some control over this by creating reasonable boundaries to protect ourselves.

An otolaryngologist I know used to go to the hospital every night to see his patients, even when he wasn't on call. He was one of two otolaryngologists in his community and couldn't say no to his patients. This meant that he missed a huge amount of his family life including his children's early years. The answer was simple: to let his partner, who was on call, see the patients. He was killing himself by doing good.

If our work served no one, it would be easy to hang it up when we get home, but because our work serves others, we tend to give until we drop. A dead doctor serves no one. If you think that you are over the edge with work commitment, see chapter 4 on workaholism and find out what to do.

Control of Your Work

This has become a huge issue in the era of managed care. We often feel as if our clinical care, our area of pride and talent, is taken from us. The survey I discussed earlier shows this to be a large and growing issue. The less control we have of our clinical care, the more frustrated and angry we become.

Health plans are an obvious target of our angst. They represent the major structural changes and loss of control for physicians in the past twenty years, as evidenced by a J. D. Power and Associates survey.[2] In this study, thirty-thousand physicians were surveyed regarding relationships with health plans. The outcomes showed that physicians want maximum independence (high need for control); 75 percent were annoyed at having to justify clinical decisions (high need for autonomy and control), 50 percent were angry about being profiled by managed care plans, and 46 percent were seriously considering leaving practice.

Are we unhappy because of health plans, or are we just unhappy and blaming the health plans. Either way, we sat around and watched it happen. We tried our hardest to get the best deals from the plans, rather than trying to stop their growth process. As it is said, "When you point a finger at someone else, three are pointing back at you." It is time for us to regain control.

This is a huge issue for all of us and an area of rapid change. In many ways the managed-care era is ending. There is little money to be made in managing care in the way that it has been done over the last twenty years. Multiple health plans are merging, closing, or being forced to cut staff and raise premiums. They are even dropping the process of case review because it doesn't amount to great savings for them. This process will likely bring us back to an indemnity-format health plan for the well-to-do and a governmental plan for the not so well-to-do.

Wherever medicine takes us over the next few decades, changes are inevitable, and we will need creativity and flexibility to survive.

We must gain emotional clarity and creativity to work proactively to re-create the way we practice and teach medicine. I don't pretend to know what the next chapter of medicine will be, but I do know that if we help create it with love and compassion toward ourselves, our families, and our patients, it will be a better version of medical care than exists today.

Gender Differences

Women physicians have more complex lives than their male colleagues. Historically, medicine has not been a warm, fuzzy place for women. While this is likely to change in the coming years as more women enter the medical workplace (greater than half of medical school enrollees are now women), it is not the happiest place for women today. Many women physicians are still looked down upon for taking time with their families or working part-time. They are seen as less than men in this regard. Here is my suggestion to the men out there who complain about part-time women physicians: deal with it; medicine is changing. Just because you may not have been able to do this in your career does not mean it is not healthy for female physicians and their patients; after all, happy doctors help make happy patients. Yes, there are inconveniences such as shift coverage and the need to juggle office space, but it's time to let go and adjust. This is the future of medicine!

There are some statistical differences documented in the woman physician's experience. In a survey study of 5,704 men and women physicians in primary and specialty non-surgical care,[3] women physicians reported a higher satisfaction with their specialties, and with patient and colleague relationships, than men but lower satisfaction with autonomy, pay, and resources. Women physicians tend to see more women patients with complex psychosocial problems, while also seeing patients with the same numbers of complex medical problems. This is because a patient with complex medical or social problems believes that a female physician will be a better listener. This is especially stressful for these physicians because every patient seems to want to talk their ears off. Thus, women are seeing more challenging patients than their male colleagues. This is additionally stressful for women physicians who are being compared to their colleagues on a patient-volume basis.

On average, women physicians reported needing 36 percent more time than allotted to provide quality care for new patients or consultations, compared with 21 percent more time needed by men. This is probably due to the complexity of the patients. While seeing more complicated patients, overall, women are paid approximately twenty-two thousand dollars less than men. However, some of this is due to choice of jobs. Women are more likely to choose salaried positions, in which the income is lower but the hours are more controlled. Generally a man and woman in the same job are paid the same. There are other work-related issues for women. Women are significantly more likely than men to pursue an academic career. But the number of women who advance to the senior ranks is much lower than the number of men.[4] In many work environments, women physicians are vulnerable to high rates of verbal abuse and physical assault by male patients as well as by other health care workers.[5] These abuses can be as subtle as an unwelcome kiss on the cheek from a colleague or patient, or as blatant as a verbal insult or physical attack.

Because of societal roles set for women, they often do more than their share of work at home, with their children, and with community activities. Women may feel that they have tried to please everyone but have pleased no one. With all of the above responsibilities, women physicians find that their personal needs are last and often lost. They put their personal and emotional needs at the bottom of the list of priorities. There is no time to consistently take care of themselves, even the basics such as exercising, eating well, getting enough sleep, and spending time alone or with friends.[6] Trying to accomplish this impossible list of life tasks is difficult for anyone and maybe impossible. Give this list of tasks to a perfectionist (as many doctors are) and it becomes a recipe for self-destruction.

I feel like I have to justify every minute I spend not taking care of someone else.

— Tish Kelley-Holmes, MD
Family Physician and mother of five children

How does this affect women physicians' mental health and attitudes? Women had 1.6 times the odds of reporting burnout compared with men. The odds of burnout for women increase by 12 percent to 15 percent for each additional five hours worked per week over forty hours. The odds of burnout were 40 percent less for women when the support of colleagues, a spouse, or significant other was present for balancing work and home issues. A lack of control in the workplace predicted burnout in women but not in men. On average, women physicians have less control over the day-to-day aspects of their practice such as the volume of patient load, selecting physicians for referrals, and details of office scheduling.3 In part, this may be due to the fact that women are more likely to give up control issues in their choice of practice in order to have greater control over the number of hours worked.

The Changing of Traditional Roles for Male Physicians Don't worry, women, the men will be catching up to your rate of burnout soon. The role of the male physician in the family is changing. Thirty years ago, a male physician, married with children, would work all day, come home to a house that was managed by a full-time homemaker spouse, and spend a short time with the family. Medicine overall was a way of life. Today the male physician is trying to do what female physicians have done all along: take care of the house, be there for the kids' activities, and be there for their spouses. This is the world of dual-income families and new roles for men. I have no doubt that we see more burnout as men try to do the same as their female colleagues.

We Are Not Alone
If it seems to you that life is more stressful than it used to be, there are data to

corroborate your feelings. Richard Rahe, co-creator of the Holmes-Rahe Life Stress Inventory, evaluated stress in American life in 1997 compared to 1964 when the scale was first presented. This scaling system gives points for major life changes such as moving, changing jobs, death of a family member, divorce, and marriage. When the authors compared average American life in 1997 to 1964, they found that, on average, life had become 46 percent more stressful than in the past.[7] You may wonder how this can be. We have become more mobile, and we change jobs and marriage partners more frequently. These changes add significant life stress.

Another view of stress in our society is within the Health Enhancement Research Organization (HERO) study. The HERO has been collecting data on employed individuals since 1990. A study published in 1998 following over forty-six thousand employed people showed that stress and depression were the most costly diagnoses reflected in medical claims. People who were depressed had health expenditures 70 percent higher than average, while those who were stressed had health expenditures 46 percent higher than average. This is most dramatic because health expenditures for diabetic individuals were only 35 percent higher than average, obese individuals 21 percent higher, smokers 20 percent higher, and hypertensive individuals 12 percent higher.[8]

When you consider that stressed and depressed people have higher physician visits, emergency room visits, and medication use, these data begin to make sense. It makes even greater sense when you also consider that the common ailments that inspire medical attention, such as GI problems, back and neck problems, and headache, are all related to emotional issues. I would also add that other complaints such as colds and flus, arrhythmias, and even coronary disease have emotional components. It starts to become obvious from how the office visits add up. A recent statement by the American Psychological Association claimed that 75 percent of all primary-care office visits were stress related. This may be an underestimate!

The most disturbing outcome of the HERO study was that 2.2 percent of participants were "depressed most of the time," and 18 percent felt stressed "most of the time." There is an epidemic of stress out there.

Key Lessons
1. We are not alone in our stress.
2. We have our hands full.
3. It is not all within your control.
4. Having babies, happy marriages, and religion help our well-being.
5. We like science.
6. We need creativity and flexibility to survive coming changes in medicine.
7. We choose our careers and workplaces; let go of the victim role.
8. Accept that medicine is changing for men and women.
9. Stop whining; it drains energy!

How Did We Get to This Place?

A CENTURY AND A HALF OF MEDICINE IN A NUTSHELL

If a majority of physicians are unhappy, this can mean one of three things: (1) they've all been infected with some undiscovered unhappiness virus; (2) there is a preselection into medicine of people with dissatisfaction tendencies; or (3) there is a mismatch among the external structure of the job they are trying to do, the way they do it, and who they are. To begin to evaluate these issues, let's look at how the structure of medicine has changed in the past 130 years. In following sections we will evaluate our internal structure to see where the mismatch occurs, and start the process of re-creating ourselves. Once we do this important work of re-creation, we can then turn our attention toward the re-creation of the system of medicine.

The Years 1870 through 1940

Medical education in the United States before the 1870s had very little consistency or predictability. Medical degrees were offered from a variety of medical colleges with a massive variety of curricula. The colleges were commercial institutions whose main interest was moving students through their doors. After all, profit is profit. There was course work, which was typically two 16-week blocks of classes, and there were apprenticeships, which were variable in experience and duration.

The late 1800s were a time of significant changes in medical education. European education was far superior to that of the United States. Major medical colleges such as Johns Hopkins and Harvard were the first to adapt some degree of consistency and purpose. The standardization of curricula slowly began here, but it wasn't until the early 1900s that any large-scale movement occurred in this direction.

In 1910, Abraham Flexner, a Louisville, Kentucky, private-school headmaster, wrote "Medical Education in the United States and Canada" as a commissioned report for the Carnegie Foundation for the Advancement of Teaching. In this report he pointed out the inconsistencies of medical education and railed the universities for their profit-motivated goals. Thus began the creation of standardized medical education in the United States. Medical schools began to adapt similar curricula and structure.

This was the beginning of the heyday of modern medicine. It also marked the beginning of a century of reductionism in medicine. Anytime a standard is created, things outside of that standard are eliminated. In this process, entire ways of practice were alienated, such as homeopathy and osteopathy. This also led to the first wave of unhappy physicians. External regulating forces told them that what they were doing was no longer considered valid medical practice, because it did not meet the standard of care. Sound familiar? Did you think this began with HMOs?

By the 1920s the commercial medical schools had been put out of business, and large universities became the seat of medical education. Students now had to pass rigorous entrance requirements. In addition, state licensure of physicians was begun. While this is conceptually admirable, the accessibility to medical education dropped significantly. Poorer students and students of multiple ethnic groups were now excluded from medical education. This then meant fewer physicians for poor and ethnic communities.

This new system of medicine was also very expensive to maintain. This was the beginning of using foundation monies to support medical education. It also meant that the costs of medical treatment would increase, therefore further decreasing access by poorer people. Better care for fewer people had begun, and the strata in care delivery began to widen.

Another stratification took place between academic physicians and physicians in private practice. It was very prestigious to be an academic faculty member. Thus was born the LMD, the local medical doctor. This is a denigrating term used commonly in the ivory tower of medical education to insult physicians in primary practices for not keeping up to date. While this was not the beginning of judgmental behavior in physicians, it sure did up the ante.

The depression left many Americans without the means to afford health care. This led to the creation of governmental health coverage, a third-party payment for health care. This enhanced reductionism in medicine (reduction in available treatments and provider type). An outside party now defined reimbursable health care. This set the stage for substantial income (through third-party payment) for physicians in the 1960s and 1970s, as well as the managed-care era.

The Year 1940 through the 1950s

This was a time of rapid growth in medicine and medical science. In this period science became the raison d'être of medicine. Brilliant new discoveries, such as penicillin, led the way toward disease cures.

World War II created a need for more doctors and nurses. Medical and nursing curricula were shortened. Students were admitted to medical schools before graduating college, in order to meet the demands for more physicians. Government loans allowed students of all backgrounds to enter the medical profession. This then created a post-war output of more physicians. If you understand the role of supply and demand, this creates greater utilization of the medical system and an overall increase in national health care expenditure.

This was also the era of the "war against disease," as stated by Vannevar Bush, Roosevelt's health advisor. Massive federal monies were spent in the search for magic bullets to cure diseases as penicillin had done for infectious disease. University research budgets increased by 900 percent in the decade the forties. This led to significant growth in the size of medical schools and to the advent of research institutions such as the NIH. This rapid growth also furthered the splitting in the medical faculty at the universities. The basic scientists were now receiving the bulk of the support for research. The clinical scientists and teachers were receiving less. Infighting for dollars became common, and the experience of the student changed dramatically. Much of the students' time was spent with basic scientists who had far less interest in patient care. The student of that era was taught less about hands-on care and emotional connection with the patient than about molecular and cellular interaction.

The patient, who in the 1800s might be known as "Mrs. Smith, the daughter of Robert Smith, the mother of Dan Smith, who had a problem with her liver humors"; in the 1930s became "Mrs. Smith with her interesting unsolved liver abnormality"; and later, in the 1950s, "the liver in room 320." In the 1960s and 1970s Mrs. Smith, became "the person with the genetic abnormality or viral infiltration who may respond to an IV infusion of X, Y, or Z." While this seems like medical progress, there are two significant problematic issues with this process: (1) the dehumanization of the patient and thus a reduction in emotional contact, and (2) an increasing cost of care for the individual.

The use of third-party insurance grew rapidly in this era. Workers' unions were demanding that health care coverage be a benefit for the employee. This led to a large population of individuals with health care coverage. The demands on the medical system increased. Due to the increased training of physicians during World War II, there was a rapid growth of practitioners available to meet this demand. The Hill-Burton Act of 1946 led to federal funding for hospital construction. Thus, there were now places to house these patients. In essence, demand accelerated supply, which then generated greater demand. This was the beginning of the salad days of medicine, all funded by the U.S. government!

The 1960s through the 1970s

These were truly the "salad and steak days" of medical care. Science was king, more and more physicians were being trained, the pharmaceutical industry was exploding, hospitals were profitable, and medical groups were lucrative. We were truly riding high!

Because medicine was so profitable, we physicians began to believe that we were great at business too. It is easy to profit when margins for profit are extraordinarily high. We created large-group infrastructures and invested in medical-related services and the companies that delivered those services. This created a massive infrastructure and overhead in our new and profitable way of delivering care, which worked well until the era of managed care.

The 1980s and 1990s

The cost of delivering health care became overwhelming. The governmental health care system became strained, and employers' contribution to health care was eroding corporate profits. The solution was to create and encourage the growth of a private industry that regulates health care cost of delivery. Thus managed care was born.

In general terms, there is nothing wrong with the concept of managed care. The system had become too expensive to maintain. If there is a limited amount of money to feed the system, as there was on the government level, the way to address this is to reduce cost of care or reduce access to care. In other countries, this was driven by the national government (as in England, for example) or through governmental control of payment (as in Canada). In the United States it would have been political suicide to reduce access to care, so a private industry grew to reduce the cost of care. This was the goal of the managed care industry and the beginning of regulations and restriction in Medicare and Medicaid coverage.

However, the outcome was less than ideal. Corporations and new branches of existing payers were created to manage this care delivery. The creation of new structural overhead was fed by the already-limited health care dollars. If the goal was to skim the excess off the system, these companies did well. In the process, however, monies that would have gone to physicians and hospitals now went to the managed-care companies, which began a flattening or decline in physician and hospital income. The salad days were over, and the battles were just beginning!

Managed care also has its limitations. If the goal is skimming off the excess, then at some point there is no more excess. When a managed health care system consumes some portion of the health care dollar, no one makes a profit, not the hospitals, the doctors, or the managed-care industry. This point in the cycle was reached in the early twenty-first century. Managed-care companies and hospitals began to close and merge, and physician incomes dropped.

We are now at a point in which health care cannot afford itself. Prices for insurance are rising, availability of coverage is shrinking, and corporate support of health coverage is on the decline. Add inflation, increases in malpractice premiums, an aging population, and rising costs of therapy, and it's no wonder we feel the crunch!

The Physician-to-Patient Ratio

As population growth exceeds the output of new physicians and as physicians retire earlier, the physician-to-patient ratio in this country is dropping dramatically. There is an effort to expand the number of new medical graduates, but as the population ages, this may not be enough.

What do we see happening today?

- Rising overhead to deliver care (including malpractice coverage)
- An expensive style of care (pharmacological and technologically based)
- Expensive training of physicians
- More physicians leaving medicine than ever before

- Physician-to-patient ratios dropping nationwide
- Decreasing coverage for more and more people
- Decreased time and contact with patients

Are you surprised that you have stress from all this?

CHAPTER 4 **The Physician Personality**

After viewing the role of system-based changes in health care, you feel at a loss to do something about your current situation. Up to this point we've only looked at the external stressors on your system. To be complete in the process of this evaluation, we must now turn our view within. Is it possible that the personality characteristics typical for physicians can add or create stress regardless of the external circumstances?

The personality traits of individuals drawn to a career of medical service are unique. By nature, we are intelligent, caring, inquisitive, and sensitive people. These are traits that help us succeed early in our pre-medical lives and are very useful in our medical lives as well. We are also competitive, obsessive, perfectionistic, and compulsive, all traits of type-A personalities. While some of these may seem like negative personality attributes, could you have survived your pre-med and medical training without these behaviors? Probably not.

It is important to acknowledge the past value of these behaviors and then to evaluate them in your current life. For example, if you were a resident who didn't know the potassium level of a diabetic on rounds the morning after patient admission, you would almost be guaranteed abuse and embarrassment by the attending physician, in front of your peers, interns, and students. In what is likely an exhausted state, obsessive-compulsive tendencies would save you the trauma of embarrassment. You may have just crawled into the call-room bed and, in that last moment of wakefulness, remembered to check the patient's potassium level. You would perseverate for a moment, find yourself unable to sleep, and then go check the level. Would the patient have been at real risk had you grabbed two hours of sleep and checked it in the morning? Maybe not. The impulse to check would be one of obsession, often driven by a self-protective need to be sure that you know the potassium level on rounds the next morning. This is the ever-present rounds fear combined with the fear of doing harm.

Do you need that response now? It was a learned response to a set of circumstances that existed many years ago. Are you still holding a fear of getting blasted if you forget to look at a diabetic's potassium on admission, or have you incorporated this self-flagellating response into your way of being? Have you substituted the lawyer, the IPA, or the medical group looking over your shoulder or for the attending physician who used to look over your shoulder? At this point in your career, isn't it reasonable to look at the labs when you get to the office or hospital rather than beat yourself up with your own catecholamines?

Let's look at how our personalities drive our behaviors. The goals of this process are to gain awareness of how we react and where our reactions come from, to acknowledge how our reactions served us, and then to begin to modify or let go of them through the tools of psychosynthesis, HeartMath, and meditation. These tools are described in detail in later chapters. I will presume that at the end of this process you will still want to be caring, inquisitive, and intelligent, so I won't spend time with those characteristics, although later in the book I'll show you how to enhance them, if you desire to do so. If you prefer to be less caring and more isolated, and have lost interest in learning, put the book down and go kick the dog around the yard for awhile; it will be more satisfying then deep personal work!

Where Do Our Behaviors Come From?

It is important to look at our behaviors as multifaceted in their genesis. Some may be biochemical in nature (such as obsessive-compulsive disorder), some are learned behaviors, and most are a mixed bag, biosocial, if you will. Tendencies toward anxiety, depression, obsession, and compulsion have all been shown to have genetic or familial relationships. However, your response to the external environment will mold how these behaviors are expressed. Shifting your response is where we have the power to make change.

Overcare: Caring and Needing to Be Needed

In their book, *The HeartMath Solution*, Doc Childre and Howard Martin describe a state of emotional being that is very common in physicians, the state of overcare. Overcare is caring run amok. When you care for someone, it is energizing. When you are cared for, this too is energizing. But when you overcare, it is energy depleting.

Have you ever sat up at 3:00 AM worrying about a patient's diagnosis or a treatment decision you've made? Does worrying serve either you or the patient? No, it is draining. You will have less energy the next day and will have done nothing to serve your patient. Your own fatigue may be a disservice to them. This is overcare. The true emotional energy keeping you awake contains a mix of rounds fear and the self-doubt, "Am I a good enough doctor?" A healthier response would be to get a good night's sleep and reevaluate the patient in the morning when you are rested. Caring is making the best choice for you and another person; overcaring is making poor choices for both of you.

Not only do we overcare, but we are also addicted to being needed. We often get love from our patients in many forms. A patient of my wife recently called at 7:00 AM to tell her that his mother had made dumplings the night before and he wanted her to have some while they were fresh. Although 7:00 AM was not terribly convenient, he had gotten up early before work to bring them to her. Not knowing where we live, he called from the parking lot of a nearby market. Moments like this, when patients say thanks and go out of their way to show you appreciation, are the highs we get as physicians. We feel valued, we feel like we are enough, and we feel loved.

The problem is that this is a form of intermittent gratification. If you recall B. F. Skinner's experiments with rats, intermittent gratification is the most powerful reinforcer of a behavior. As we are rewarded intermittently with gratitude from our patients, we end up seeking gratitude more vigorously. Because of this, we tend to get upset when patients don't thank us, especially after we have gone out of our way for them. We then work harder and harder, expecting more gratitude. This leads us to overextend ourselves in order to be appreciated. Our self-care then suffers. In the language of the addiction world, this is known as codependency. We are so busy caring for others that we no longer take care of ourselves. The solution is one of the most difficult tasks known to man, to learn to love yourself enough to know that you are enough. If you come close to this, you no longer need external validation to get your highs.

Perfectionism

Tom, a forty-seven-year-old pediatrician, is highly dedicated to taking care of his patients. His charts are immaculate, his notes are precise and well written, and his diagnostic testing is always rigorous. He loves the hard cases and spends evenings pouring over his textbooks at home. He always works later than the other physicians, is always running behind, and never seems able to catch up. He wakes up at night worried about patients and is concerned that he might have missed something in his evaluation of them. He is fatigued and frustrated. His wife is very frustrated as well, but doesn't say anything because medicine is so important to Tom.

Perfectionism is extremely common among our colleagues, although it has not been measured as such. It is often excused because we often deal with life-and-death issues. This fosters the belief that mistakes are inexcusable. If a physician is imperfect, he or she is a bad physician. We are all fallible; we physicians all make mistakes, as do the rest of the humans on the planet. This paradox can create significant stress for us.

If you see twenty-five patients daily, five days a week (for many of us, it's more), forty-eight weeks per year for fifty years, that's 300,000 clinical decisions made. (How many of you perfectionists checked my math or applied your own numbers?) When you consider that we usually multitask while making clinical decisions, this number grows substantially. With this in mind, what is the likelihood that one of 300,000 decisions was the wrong one? The dean of the medical school at University of Toronto once told his incoming class, "Half of what we teach you in the next four years in wrong, and the problem is, we don't know which half." How can this be true? Medicine is always changing and therefore what is true today may not be true tomorrow. This brings your average hit rate down to 50 percent. If you add the fact that we are fallible and that there are variances for people's responses to medicines, you may be correct 30 to 40 percent of the time. Don't feel bad; in baseball, the greats have a batting average of 40 percent (400), so you are still up there!

The problem for us is that we chastise ourselves for these errors and fear that others will do so as well. We worry and hold anxiety about our mistakes for years. I still hold some anxiety about a misdiagnosed testicular cancer that fortunately was picked up by a colleague of mine. That was over fifteen years ago! Later in this book I will describe to you how anxiety and fear of errors increases the risk of errors. A healthier state is to be aware of errors, expecting that they will happen now and then. When an error is made, be thankful that you caught it, and learn from the mistake.

It is also important to realize that generally, we have no one to discuss these mistakes with. We are afraid to talk to our coworkers because we don't want to be seen as imperfect; we know we'll be judged. We don't want to trouble our spouses with this information because they may not understand or we may fear their judgment as well. Often, what is behind this is our own insecurity. The underlying self-doubt is, "are we good enough?"

Where did this perfectionism come from? Much of this behavior is learned from our parents. Rachael Naomi Remen, a wonderful physician and author, describes a scene from her childhood that exemplifies this perfectly. She had achieved an A in all of her subjects except math. She decided that she would show her dad that she was capable of making an A in math, and applied herself to the task. She recalls coming home to her father with a math test score of 98 and very excitedly telling him about it. His response was, "What happened to the other two points?" This encapsulates the dynamic of perfectionism perfectly.

As children, we wanted to please our parents. Depending on the particular relationship, this need can be driven by seeking love and support, or it may be to avoid discomfort. Our parent may have held lofty goals and expectations for us and often believed that it was in our best interest to go for the gold. The belief is prevalent in our country that shooting for the stars will facilitate your doing well even if you fall slightly short of this goal.

On a superficial level this may seem viable; however, look at the effect of the simple interaction described above on a young child. The child was excited by her achievement. If she had received support from her father, she would have been motivated to continue this good work, as it would've served her goal of feeling loved and validated. She would have developed a healthy self-esteem and continued to learn without anxiety. She would also have probably gained greater confidence and creativity, which she would've then brought into other relationships and tasks in her adult life.

In the scenario above, the child was taught to question her own validity and would thus feel insecure. She would also continue to seek her father's love and support by pushing herself harder. As no child is perfect, there would be other less-than-perfect outcomes and therefore continued disappointments. This would lead to an adult who is a successful person with significant insecurity. Again, looking at the B. F. Skinner model of intermittent gratification, this child would become an adult who pushes herself toward perfection and is rarely, if ever, satisfied with her performance. This would affect adversely her adult relationships, as she too would expect perfection of others and be critical of their performances.

One way that this process manifests is the seeking of socially significant goals, such as choosing a career that is difficult to obtain, rigorous to live, socially admired, and financially rewarding. Sound familiar? This would be a less harsh, socially acceptable manifestation of the drive to please. Many of us choose medicine to please our parents. This may be at a deep or subconscious level, but I ask you to consider this in your own choice of career. It is an enormous amount of work in order to gain approval from your parents!

Our parents are not the only ones whose approval we seek. We seek the approval of our mentors in our training and even our patients. In a simplistic way we want to be perceived as perfect. If perfection were obtainable, this might be a good goal; however, as we all make mistakes, none of us will ever achieve perfection, and many of us will remain unsatisfied with our performance and ourselves. How sad. I would choose to be happily imperfect any day of the week; it's much less stressful. Just acknowledging your imperfection will be freeing for you.

I am not saying that you should give up the concept of bettering yourself. This would lead to stagnation. I ask that you accept that the goal is to be better, not perfect. If the goal is perfection, you can't win! My mentor in medical school taught me to ask, "What have I done today that I could do better tomorrow?" He never said, "What could I do perfectly tomorrow?" Better can be good enough!

> *Anything worth doing is worth doing half-assed.*
>
> — Rachael Naomi Remen, MD

Keep in mind that trying to live up to another's expectations is a way of allowing them to control your life. Many of us came to this in our teen years; rebellion was the outcome. Take back your personal power! Choose your own goals, not those held by others.

Other expectations we try to live up to may be social. For example, if you were married during your training, your spouse lived through difficult times. You may feel obligated to pay them back with a nice house, car travel, or other rewards. While this appears to be valid on a social level, it may not work for you or your family. If you feel overworked because you are trying to do good things for you family, in essence, to be the provider, you may want to ask them if they would prefer more income or more of your time. You may be shocked to find out that the time spent with you is more important than a new car or vacation, but you won't know until you ask. In a *Wall Street Journal* survey, 54 percent of children aged three –to twelve years said that they would prefer their parents be less stressed and tired from work. You can't ask for a more honest authority than your kids.

Let me share with you the story of a wonderful fellow physician I met in Northern California. An anesthesiologist came up to me after a lecture and shared an incredible story with me. He is a first-generation immigrant to the United States. In his country of origin, his family was very poor. He believed that the best thing he could do for his family was to make sure that they lived in the best house in the best neighborhood. He sent the children to the best schools. He and his wife drove great cars and also tried to save money. In order to do this, he worked twelve to fourteen hours each day. This fell apart one day when he received a call from a family friend, a lawyer, who mentioned that his wife had asked him about divorce proceedings. At the mention of this, our friend, the doctor, had enough caring and clear headedness to have a long overdue conversation with his wife.

She told him that, even though she appreciated the nice possessions and comfortable lifestyle they had, she felt as if she didn't have a husband and that the children had no father. He had made the mistake of projecting his own expectations and values onto his family. They wanted him more than the nice cars, houses, and vacations. Luckily, this couple had enough structure and perseverance to seek counseling, Ten years later, they live in a smaller house, drive smaller cars, and take less-extravagant vacations, but they have a happier and more fulfilling life together!

Perfectionism also inspires harsh judgments of others. Previously I mentioned that the development of the academic white tower of medicine leads to the creation of demeaning terms for nonacademic physicians. This is an unfair judgment. How many of you talked about the LMD (local medical doc) during training and are now an LMD yourself? How does it feel to know that someone may be judging you at this very moment? It certainly isn't energizing and it's not fair. Only we can stop that process by accepting each other's vulnerability and limitations.

In one of my workshops a physician in his late fifties expressed that one of his biggest stressors was cleaning up the mistakes made by his colleagues with patients. I asked him how often this happened. He responded that it occurred with 90 percent of his consults. I then asked him how long this had been a problem. He responded that it had been that way for his entire career, over thirty years. I then suggested to him that his bar might be too high and that he was judging his colleagues far too harshly. His wife told the group that he behaved similarly with her and everyone they knew. Perfectionism can be pervasive and destructive for your entire life.

Perfectionism also leads to self-criticism and self-abuse. This may be the most detrimental of all types of judgment. If we cannot achieve perfect outcomes, we tend to beat ourselves up for it. We become our own harshest and most persistent critics. The problem is that we don't know how to let go. We hold the belief that the more we push ourselves, the more likely we are to succeed in our goal toward perfection. As perfection is illusory, we will spend the rest of our days beating ourselves up. What a waste of time and energy! Learn to accept yourself as imperfect. Learn from any errors you make. Apologize if needed, and move on!

Most of my clinical and research work is in cardiovascular prevention. I haven't a clue about the latest antibiotics or chemotherapeutic agents, yet whenever someone used to ask me about these things, I had a twinge of guilt for not knowing. At times, in order to seem perfect, I even confabulated around these questions. Now, when I'm feeling centered, I say the three hardest words in the medical language, "I don't know," and will look up the answer if it's useful to do so.

The inability to admit not knowing an answer is a learned behavior. As young children, many of us were encouraged to ask questions and concede when we didn't have the answers. Not knowing was okay and encouraged. We presumed that the adults had the answers. In our early teens we probably heard, "You are old enough to know better." This attitude was reinforced throughout our youth to the point of embarrassment if we did not know an answer. Medical training only made this worse. On rounds or in morning report, it was unacceptable to not know an answer, and we were made to feel inadequate if we didn't know, thus generating generalized anxiety and a sense of incompetence .

Learn to say, "I don't know, but if you'd like, I can find out for you." You will feel less pressure, and the people you serve will appreciate your integrity and your desire to serve them. Not a bad trade-off for a little imperfection!

Competitiveness
The underlying question behind perfectionism is, "Am I enough?" The same question and fear drives us toward competitiveness, although we tend to think of it as, "Am I good enough to survive?"

By definition, we are some of the most intelligent people in our community. Generally, grade school and even high school were no challenge to us. We knew how to rise to the academic occasion. At that time in our lives we had little academic anxiety; we were at the top of our game!

For many of us, our first academic challenge came in college. Many college courses were easy, but all of a sudden we were surrounded by people with the same ambitions we had. We also knew that all pre-meds do not make it into medical school, and we knew that there were pre-med screening courses that separated the men from the boys.

Such an experience might raise the following inner dialogue: "I have always wanted to be a doctor. My parents and friends expect this of me. I can't let them or me down. We've already invested so much time and money into my education. It can't go to waste. I must succeed, yet there are all these pre-med students around me. Some of us will make it, others won't. I must be among the ones who make it!"

For some students this inner dialogue leads to cheating. For others (hopefully few), it leads to a nasty attitude. For most students, it just causes anxiety. When under stress, the usual response of resourceful persons is to push themselves harder. One day, a student walks out of what seemed like a very difficult exam to hear a friend say, "That was no big deal." This leads to increasing anxiety, which prompts the need to push harder. Other students may not seem to be working as hard, but the reality is that they are just pretending. The anxiety brings up the "Am I enough?" voice and the need to push harder still. This cycle — anxiety, "Am I enough?" push, anxiety, "Am I enough?" — continues and worsens throughout medical studies. By the end of your education you've spent eight years feeling fearful and competitive, and doubting your abilities.

If you think the competitive attitude just drifts away after all this, think again. It is probably with you to this day and won't dissipate until you work on it. I recently attended a powerful self-insight program called The Hoffman Process (see www.hoffmaninstitute.org). In this process, I realized that I was still in competition with my wife. We had met in medical school and there was always friendly competition between us. By looking at this, I realized that friendly competition was as harmful emotionally as friendly fire. At some deep level, I needed to be better than she was. Fortunately, I am working on recovering from this mind-set. Later in this book you will have the opportunity to look at these issues within yourselves, but for now, accept that competitiveness exists and look at how it affects your life, friends, and family, if not just your own catecholamines and cortisol levels.

Type-A Behavior Pattern

The competitiveness, perfectionism, anxiety, and high goal orientation are significant components of what Meyer Friedman, MD, defined as a type-A personality.

As an example of type-A behavior, let me describe how I got into medical school. In college I had a GPA of 3.6. Not bad, but not med-school material in the late 1970s, when competition was extreme. As a college senior, my thirty-plus applications for medical school led to thirty-plus rejection letters. This was extremely frustrating and made me very angry. Sure, my school record was not 4.0, but did these jerks know what a great guy I was and how caring I was? This is typical type A, and not only type A but angry type A. At that moment, it was all about me!

As a card-carrying, obsessive type A, I signed up for a one-year, non-thesis masters program in physiology. I knew that if I scored a 4.0 in a masters program, I would be a shoe in. What did I get the next year? Thirty-plus rejection letters.

I decided that I needed to work in a medical school in order to get in. I wanted to live in Washington, D.C., so I went door to door to all the physiology and neurophysiology research labs in the three D.C.-area medical schools to get a job. This worked; I got a job, and the next year, I was in medical school.

All of this seemed functional at the time. I had a goal, and I used my resources and wits to achieve that goal. I persisted over three years and obtained an additional degree to accomplish the goal. But I was also angry, frustrated, and anxious.

The traits of a type-A personality are as follows:

- Opinionated
- Judgmental of others
- Pressured to succeed
- Habitually using a clipped pattern of speaking and forced smiles
- Victim of "hurry sickness" (always rushing against time)
- A multitasker
- Aggressive beyond the need of the situation
- Distrustful of others to do the job right
- Perfectionistic
- Competitive
- Need to be recognized for their accomplishments
- Need to prove self-worth through performance

Many of these traits may sound familiar to you. Many of them seemed necessary to survive medical school and training, but how many of them serve you well today? Type-A behavior is strongly associated with coronary disease and cardiac mortality. It certainly doesn't serve your health. We tend to hold onto this behavior because many of its aspects are associated with societal and financial success, resulting in the underlying belief that if we let type-A behavior go, our success will diminish.

My favorite exhibition of these patterns is chronic lateness. Are you always (or mostly) ten to fifteen minutes late for anything? This is from a mixture of hurry sickness and multitasking. For example, suppose you have ten minutes before you need to leave for an event or appointment. You suddenly think of something that needs to get done. Invariably you find a task to do in those ten minutes, but it is usually something that would take twenty minutes. Now you are ten minutes late. Does this pattern sound familiar? Next time you do this, think of how you feel when someone keeps you waiting for ten or twenty minutes. Are you anymore important than they are?

Another classic example of physician type-A behavior is based in the high need for control. The typical physician will give a task to an employee, and then watch the employee begin to do the task in a different way from how the physician would do the task. This makes the physician anxious to the point of jumping in to fix the situation. Such a fix-it situation is driven by a high need for control and a need to be the fixer in the white hat. The outcome of this behavior is as follows:

- The physician ends up doing everything.
- The employee learns not to put effort into a task, because the physician is going to take over anyhow (passive-aggressive behavior).
- The employee's creativity is squelched and de-energized.
- The physician loses the opportunity to learn from an employee who might have a new way of doing the task.

This is the definition of a "lose-lose situation," all because of your type-A tendencies. How can you begin to undo this behavior and facilitate your staff's creativity? Give them tasks that are achievable, let them make mistakes, and then try again. Remember to congratulate your staff for their successes. I ask that you treat your own children this way as well. Let them try, congratulate them for successes, and work with them when they don't succeed. Remember that their definition of success may vary from yours and only through trying will they learn.

I challenge you with this statement; a type A and a type B (relaxed, but busy behavior) can get the same amount of work done each day. The only difference is that the type A does it with anxiety and hostility. Which do you want to be?

In chapter 15, "Psychosynthesis," we will address these behaviors and work through them to better understand how they serve you and how they disserve you.

Safety-Seeking Behavior

The average American businessperson changes jobs once every five to six years. In medicine, a change in career path is infrequent, if ever, and traumatic when it occurs. Why is this?

I believe that the individual attracted to medicine is attached to an unwritten societal contract. The contract states that becoming a doctor means spending a life of service to the community. We accept these terms for four reasons:

1. It's socially acceptable and the "right" thing to do.
2. We are driven to be physicians, so much so that we sign on for anything.
3. We want to have job security.
4. We are averse to change.

Honestly I believe the last two are the main drivers of the contract. The type of person who desires a medical career does not want to change jobs but wants a guaranteed good income.

The other clauses of the contract are that if you give up eight-plus years of your life to become a doctor, society will take care of you and put you in a position of high respect.

Unfortunately, the contract is falling apart! The security of medicine is dwindling. Our patients change doctors with greater frequency. We come out of our training with huge debt. We are sued more frequently, and in many ways more randomly, and our income, relative to overhead, is decreasing. "You're not in Kansas anymore, Dorothy." In that regard, Kansas isn't even Kansas anymore. The world has changed.

This adds to our stress, and as safety-seeking individuals, it rocks our nature of being. We must learn to gain flexibility and resiliency, and to reevaluate our roles as physicians. I hope to help you do this proactively through the Finding Balance process, not reactively, as most of us do.

Social Isolation

Social isolation, or lack of social embeddedness, has been associated with increased risk of cancer and heart disease. This will be discussed and reviewed in detail in chapter 13, "Connection and Communication." Social isolation is highly prevalent among physicians, even though we tend think of ourselves as social people.

How do we become socially isolated? It starts when we are very young. By nature many of us tend toward quietness and doing well in school. We tend to be nerds or at least closet nerds in high school. We are often less involved in athletics and more in academia. This supports a sense of social isolation, as it makes us feel different from our classmates. In addition we are also self-motivated and have a high need for control. Therefore we don't work well in teams, by nature. This too contributes to our isolation.

Putting such individuals in programs where they work eighty-hour weeks, while their age cohorts have families, jobs, and active social lives, further enhances a sense of social isolation. If such persons are also afraid to discuss their mistakes and vulnerabilities, they become more distant. When a high need for control makes perfectionistic individuals feel that their lives are out of control, they will shut themselves off for fear of appearing imperfect. When they feel that their families and friends outside of medicine won't understand what they are going through, this seals the coffin. It's no surprise that a majority of physicians feel a sense of isolation.

The simple answer to this dilemma is to allow yourself to be imperfect, out of control, and vulnerable with those who love you. Learn from your mistakes, and work toward better, not perfect.

The Medical Training Process and Our Personalities

Let's now take a competitive, type-A, perfectionistic, safety-seeking, social isolate and put them through eight or more years of intensive training. Ouch!

The way we train individuals to be physicians is in many ways dysfunctional and contributes to our own dysfunctional behaviors. It enhances the previously described personality traits and tends to overwhelm the trainee with excessive information and responsibility. This would appear to be a basic tenant of our training. Overload students or residents with responsibility and they will rise to the occasion. And we do rise to the occasion. We work longer hours, get paid barely enough to survive (especially considering the debt accrued in education and lost opportunity), and see more and more patients. This becomes a way of being, because we are in this state for so long.

Emotional Dissociation

The emotionally dissociated state is one that we adopt to survive difficult moments in medicine. For example, when managing an emergency, we are taught to shut down our emotions and be the best objective physician we can. We are told that this will serve our patients best. We also do this during such moments as anatomy lab. When confronted with an adverse circumstance (no one enjoys the smell of formaldehyde or working on a dead body), we shut off our emotions and try to stay in the mind-set of scientist and student. This too is an emotionally dissociated state.

In the emergency room or in anatomy lab, this is a very functional and useful defense mechanism. It allows the physician to perform noxious or difficult tasks that may be necessary at the moment. However, after years of use, this state becomes a fall-back emotional state for physicians confronted with difficult life circumstances. It is often easier for physicians to become emotionally dissociated when dealing with illness in their families and significant relationship issues. Examples of this have been taken from the *British Medical Journal:*

> *Being married to a doctor isn't at all what I thought. Allen never tells me how he feels or asks me how I feel, yet he expects me to field his calls and protect him from the outside world. I married him because I love him, but I got a representation of an institution, not a man.*
>
> *What if I really get sick and need constant care and attention? I can't face that Jim is so distant and cool when I'm sick. Who will take care of me?[1]*

This is how, later in life, emotional dissociation causes disruption. How many times have you made the mistake of being the doctor when you should have been the spouse, parent, or child? When faced with trauma, it is wise to look at the scenario with consciousness and decide who you need to be. We will look at this in chapter 15, "Psychosynthesis."

Medical Student Abuse

If, at times, during your training, you felt as if you were treated unfairly, you are not alone. In a recent survey of 2,884 students from sixteen medical schools in the United States, 42 percent reported harassment and 84 percent reported belittlement during their medical school experience. The sources of the abuses were as follows: other students (11 and 32 percent respectively), residents (27 and 71 percent), pre-clinical professors (9 and 29 percent), clinical professors (21 and 63 percent), and patients (25 and 43 percent). Only 13 percent of students classified any of these experiences as severe.

Students who were harassed or belittled were more likely to be stressed, depressed, and suicidal; to drink alcohol or to binge drink; and to state that their faculty did not care about medical students. They were also significantly less likely to be glad they trained to become a doctor.[2]

What does abuse lead to? Further abuse. Unfortunately, as in abusive family situations, the abused becomes the abuser. This has been the trend in medicine for generations. Abuse leads to anger, hostility, exhaustion, lack of control, and post-traumatic stress disorder.

Post-Traumatic Stress Disorder-Complex Type

In the training process, most physicians develop post-traumatic stress disorder (PTSD)-complex type. This is a form of PTSD that develops over years of traumatic events. Most people think of PTSD as occurring in response to individual events such as kidnappings, wars, and other atrocities. PTSD-complex type occurs when the events are subtler, but the exposure is of long duration. Medical training can easily be considered as such an event or series of events.

The contributing factors to this type of PTSD are abuse, lack of sleep, separation from loved ones, and exposure to significantly emotionally upsetting circumstances (e.g., trauma, illness, cadavers, surgery, bone marrow aspirations, spinal taps, and many other traumatic moments).

PTSD is a symptom complex. Its symptoms may already sound familiar to you, as most of us tend to develop some degree of PTSD in our training. The key symptoms are intrusions, avoidance, and hyperarousal.

Intrusions Intrusions are spontaneous thoughts accompanied by uncomfortable emotions. How often do you dream of the hospital or school? For most people in training, the answer is many times a week. For the first few years post-training, it may be once a week or month. Even many years after training, physicians sometimes still experience these dreams. I occasionally have dreams where I am a resident all over again. Sometimes the hospital is not the one where I did my residency, but the emotional content is just as real. Some night, you may find yourself back in medical school or residency if you have not already. This is a form of intrusion. These dreams are generally not warm and fuzzy and may be very unsettling. Other intrusions can occur when you are relaxing or having fun and a flash memory occurs about the hospital or school. Such memories can be triggered by a smell or by seeing someone who resembles someone you knew in training. Again, this scenario is not always a pleasant or welcome occurrence. For a moment, think of the smell of formaldehyde. Where does your mind go? How do you feel? This is an intrusion, an external or internal cue that brings about uncomfortable emotions.

Avoidance Avoidance is the tendency to withdraw socially when feeling overloaded. It can also be accompanied by self-destructive behaviors, and such feelings as anger or depression. As physicians are, by nature, social isolates (we enjoy being alone), withdrawal is enhanced when we are overburdened. This is especially true for men who like to go hide after a particularly rough day. Women, on the other hand, tend to want to talk it out with someone. This too is one of God's little jokes on us; when both of us have had a bad day, one spouse wants to hide and the other wants to talk!

Hyperarousal Hyperarousal is the tendency to jump when startled, usually associated with stimuli such as a pager or phone ringing. This catecholamine response to a noxious stimulus is a learned response. When you got your first pager, you were probably excited to be a real doctor! Then, quietly sitting on the toilet, reading a magazine, the pager goes off, interrupting your moment of solitude. Soon the pager interrupts meals, sleep, and even sex. You begin to associate the pager with interruptions and annoyance. This sets off a catecholamine response with each page, thus a learned experience. The mid-brain interprets the pager as a noxious stimulus. You and Pavlov's dogs are in the same boat. The good news is that any learned response can be unlearned. Stress management tools can help you unlearn this response.

Workaholism in Medicine

What if there were a substance that made you stay away from home until very late and kept you awake at night? What if this substance created multiple family problems to the point of destroying your marriage? What if this substance decreased your efficiency and your ability to concentrate, and made you irritable and fatigued? What if this substance increased your risk of back problems, gastrointestinal disorders, heart disease, and stroke? What if you felt that discontinuing the use of this substance meant that your success and your self-definition would cease to be?

This is often how addicts feel about their drug of choice. They are so identified with the drug that they would lose themselves without it. On seeing a patient with these self-destructive tendencies, most of us would try to convince them to seek therapy or find other forms of help to eradicate the destructive substance from their lives. Unfortunately this is how many practicing physicians begin to approach the work of medicine. We become work addicted!

The practice of medicine becomes our drug of choice. We live in a culture that supports the practice of medicine above all else, which can often exclude our families and our health. If we stopped being a doctor, who would we be? Unlike alcoholism, workaholism is rewarded with accolades and financial success, making it a very difficult process to stop. A workaholic has lost the ability to slow down and find value in anything other than work. Workaholism is a compulsive behavior and is probably related to other compulsive behaviors and addictions. I tend to think of it as a tendency that can be modified by learning new behaviors, but for some, the compulsion is so invasive that medical treatment may be needed.

Workaholism is not measured by the number of hours you give to work. If that were the case, you would all be workaholics at this point in your career. It is more about the way you approach work and how it controls you and your ability or inability to focus on things unrelated to your career. Workaholism can also be measured by how work affects your life outside of medicine. If you have trouble shutting off your thoughts about your work and career, you may be a workaholic.

Intriguingly a wonderful psychiatrist friend of mine, upon filling out the work addiction test (below), realized the level of his work addiction. When we got into discussion about this, he insisted, "But I love my work." I then asked if his work has had an adverse effect on his life. His response was, "On my first marriage, yes." This is work addiction. If work is damaging your health and relationships, you may wish to consider this as a possibility.

We are often in denial about these behaviors because they feel productive. In a workshop, one colleague told me that she could cut down on her work anytime she wanted to. On saying these words, which many alcoholics in treatment have said to her, she knew that she was stuck!

The Genesis of Workaholism

How can this work addiction happen? The answer is fairly simple: it is a natural tendency, reinforced by learned habits. As young grade-school or high-school students, we were driven to succeed. This meant long hours of study, often balanced with long hours invested in hobbies and extracurricular activities. Generally, we put more into a day and probably got more out of a day than our friends and co-students. This excessive lifestyle leads to such rewards as success, external validation, and even love from our parents. This is a hard combination to beat, which perpetuates the behavior into our next career, that of a college student.

In college, the goal was entrance into medical school. We knew that not everyone would achieve this goal, and therefore, we worked hard for the best grades and the best records, which often included jobs, community service, and extracurricular activities. There were long days indeed, validated by the accolades of our professors and the ultimate validation, medical school admission.

Medical school requires no external activities to fill up a week. Studying and attending classes generally means that your weekdays and weekends are full. Some of us rise to the challenge (compulsion?) to go beyond this, with research projects and other school-related activities. At this point, while some extracurricular project might further your career, isn't medical school enough for you?

This seems to be the beginning of the slippery slope for many of us. Surviving medical school is difficult enough. Having a life outside of medical school is a challenge. Maintaining friendships, marriages, and other interests is challenging, yet those of us who are workaholics continue to add to our plates. This was I early in my career; not only did I have a busy practice and run a cardiac rehab program in the evening, I was also president of an elementary school board, father of two, and husband of a physician. It is at this point where the compulsion to work, or I should say, the anxieties created by not working, can begin to take over our lives.

For many of us, problems at work are easier to manage than problems at home. At work, we are in charge; we make decisions and people listen to us. How often does this happen at home? When physicians' home lives become difficult, they use work as a way of avoiding the home issues. This makes the home issues worse, leading to breakups of families and disconnection from our children.

> *John , a forty-five-year-old cardiac surgeon, was a driven, compulsive doctor, dedicated to his work. When his wife, Mary, suggested that they take a vacation to celebrate his graduation from medical school, he objected, saying that the immediate start of his postgraduate training made that impossible. So she bided her time, tolerating the unremitting grind of residency and specialty training, until he finished. Then she again suggested taking a bit of extended time together. Again, he refused, citing the demands of starting a practice, promising that they would take that long-delayed vacation together "…just as soon as I have established my practice." The automatic nature of this response was clear when subsequent proposals to do something were met with new reasons: "…just as soon as I have a partner to cover during my absence." Then, "…as soon as our group practice is well established." Ultimately Mary quit asking, backed away from the relationship, and developed a professional life of her own.[1]*

Supporting Workaholism — The System of Medicine
Is workaholism perpetuated by our system of medicine? Of course, it is. When a resident admits a large number of cases on a given night, it is a badge of honor, a form of one-upmanship. When any house staff member goes the extra mile to get research articles for the team, he or she is applauded, especially if it meant losing sleep. When physicians join a practice and put in extra hours and extra calls, and see extra patients, which often means more income, they are embraced immediately. Freud might describe this as a pathological drive to

seek parental approval. Carl Jung might describe it as a pathological need to be perceived as good above all else. Whatever way you slice it, whatever excuses you have for supporting workaholism, if it hurts your family and increases your mortality, it's not healthy!

Supporting Workaholism — The Family

Our families often contribute to the problem of workaholism. The most obvious form of this is parental approval for our hard work. We all receive this sometimes, but some of us seek it more than others, which may from a lack of constant support and approval. Excessive approval seeking is most often seen when approval is intermittent. A classic example of this is the alcoholic parent, who, when sober, can be loving and supportive, but when drunk, is abusive, unloving, and unsupportive. Again, back to B. F. Skinner, who, in his studies of animals, demonstrated that intermittent gratification is the strongest reinforcer of a behavior. The child who gets intermittent love seeks it with greatest vigor.

Does a parent need to be an alcoholic to give intermittent love? No, the workaholic parent can do this as well. This type of parent is often fatigued, obsessed with work-related issues, and emotionally unavailable to the child. This can be blatant or subtle. Have you ever lost it with your child because you were overwhelmed with work or school? Have you ever answered your cell phone when you were supposed to be spending quality time with your child? How many baseball games, dance recitals, or school plays have you missed in the name of work or school? While these behaviors appear to be more socially acceptable when compared with the behaviors of an enraged alcoholic parent, the cumulative effect on the child can be equally devastating in the long run. How available were your parents? Did they promote workaholism? Are you perpetuating that behavior?

Supporting Workaholism — The Perfect Parent

It's not just our families of origin who support our workaholic tendencies. Once these tendencies are ingrained, we physicians take them to the max. The combination of perfectionism and workaholism is very dangerous for all those involved. You want to give your child the perfect life, making sure that he or she gets into the perfect school, chooses the perfect career, and marries the perfect spouse. This behavior is rampant in the "me generation." I think of it as "baby-boomers' syndrome." No child could emotionally survive such pressure! At least your child will have something to share with a therapist in the future. This type of behavior leads to the idea of the supermom or -dad. The belief is that you can do all and be all to everyone. (Please forgive the stereotypes below, but you'll get the point.) The supermom can bake, clean, spend time with her children, manage a home, coach a sport, have a loving relationship with her partner, and be the CEO of a multinational corporation or have a full-time medical practice. Anyone who has tried to be all of these will be a burnout within five years, if not sooner. The superdad can be the coach, scout leader, loving partner, and parent, and still hold a full-time job. Again, the result is guaranteed exhaustion! Give either of these roles to a perfectionist, and *bang!* Disaster!

Supporting Workaholism — Codependency

The family can also perpetuate workaholism with codependency. Codependency is the support of a dysfunctional behavior, even though that behavior is detrimental to the lives of those involved. This is the spouse of the alcoholic who says, "Well, he never drinks in the morning." It is a passive way of supporting a dysfunctional behavior. "Well, she is taking care of sick people, even though we have no life" is the medical version. In an extreme form, codependency is the active support or allowance of the dysfunctional behavior with a lack of ability to control the behavior.

> *It still baffles me. George is never around when I need him. But when the phone rings and the hospital calls, he's so willing and ready to go. I can't tell him how I feel. He gets so uptight and defensive, and then I feel guilty. After all, he does save lives and heal the sick. How can my modest needs compete with that?[1]*

In the above quote, the spouse's guilt is an example of codependency. The spouse is disabled by her guilt to attempt to change the physician's behavior. Doing work that is good for others becomes the rationale for perpetuating or allowing behaviors that are harmful to our relationships and our health. It is no wonder that, in medicine, our divorce rates are skyrocketing!

An additional dysfunctional aspect of codependency can occur when the spouse allies with the children against the workaholic parent. This is called *triangulation*. In this process, the spouse, who feels powerless against the workaholic partner, creates a bond with their children by whining and complaining to them about the workaholic parent. Workaholics can then begin to feel like outsiders in their own homes. Whenever they are there, they feel like everyone gangs up on them. This makes home a less comfortable place to be, which only enhances tendencies to stay at work. This is a complicated cycle to get into and out of.

Although it may be subtle, most workaholism is based in primary codependence. Physicians need the accolades of others to feel valued!

Codependency — Care Addiction Test

The test below will help you evaluate the role of care dependency in your life. It is taken from Bryan E. Robinson's book, *Chained to the Desk: A Guidebook for Workaholics, Their Partners, and Children, and the Clinicians Who Treat Them* (New York University Press, 1998). If you score high on this test, I suggest you read *Chained to the Desk*.

Please answer the following questions:

1 = never true, 2 = sometimes true, 3 = often true, 4 = always true

____ I get overly involved by taking on other people's problems.

____ I feel overly responsible when bad things happen and feel that it is my role to make them better.

____ I overidentify with others by feeling their emotions as if they were my own.

____ I have an ongoing urge to take care of other people.

____ I neglect my own needs in favor of caring for the needs of others.

____ I take life too seriously and find it heard to play and have fun.

____ I have a need to solve people's problems for them.

____ I have not dealt with a lot of painful feelings from my past.

____ I feel unworthy of love.

____ I never seem to have enough time for myself.

____ I criticize myself too much.

____ I am afraid of being abandoned by those I love.

____ My life always seems to be in crisis.

____ I don't feel good about myself if I am not doing something for someone else.

____ I don't know what to do if I am not caring for someone.

____ Whatever I do never seems to be enough.

____ I have dedicated my life to helping others.

____ I get high from helping people with their problems.

____ I have a need to take charge of most situations.

____ I spend more time caretaking than I do spending time with friends, on hobbies, or on leisure-time activities.

____ It is hard for me to relax when I am not caring for others.

____ I experience emotional fatigue and compassion burnout.

____ It is hard for me to keep emotional boundaries by saying no when someone wants to tell me about a problem.

____ I have developed health or physical problems from stress, worry, or burnout.

____ I seek approval and affirmation from others through people-pleasing and by overcommitting myself.

Scoring:

25–29 You are not care addicted.

50–69 You are mildly care addicted.

70–100 You are highly care addicted.

Supporting Workaholism — The Community

Our communities also support our workaholic tendencies. Everyone loves the doctor who is always available, who can always be paged or has his cell phone on at 3:00 AM. Medical history (myth?) supports and applauds the physician who makes house calls day or night and who can be at the bedside of all patients in need.

Let us visit the small town doc of the early 1900s. This small town physician knows the community well and also is well known by the community. They know each other's families and understand each other's needs. This works, because in this model, the physician is cared for by the community; that is, the community takes care of the doctor as much as the doctor takes care of the community. When the doctor is fatigued, the community has good boundaries about not straining the doctor. When the doctor's family is in need, the community will help out. This scenario has been idealized in literature and in Norman Rockwell paintings. In some parts of the country, this scenario may still be alive and well. The physician is loved, respected, and cared for. The income is modest but sufficient, and the townspeople create reasonable boundaries for the physician. Most importantly, the patient load is minimized by the size of the population.

While this scenario is attractive and may be the goal for many of us, it is becoming more difficult to find. In part this is due to the growth of the population (more people needing more health care coverage = more patients), as well as our own predisposition to live in active, attractive regions of the country. These areas have large populations and higher costs of living, so a modest income may no longer suffice. Once the overhead of practice begins to rise, the need for income will push the modest patient load up, diminishing connection; thus, we have the death of the Norman Rockwell, picture-perfect physician model. The barefoot doctor gets shoes!

> *Work is the refuge of people who have nothing better to do.*
>
> — Oscar Wilde

The Workaholic's Inability to Play Well with Others

You may think it would be great if your partners were workaholics. Then, they would get more done. There is a flaw in this idea because the workaholic is not a team player. Workaholics have a high need for control and therefore feel that their way of doing the job is the best way. While they may pretend to listen to others' opinions, they usually do it their way. Because of this, they will not delegate well and will continually add to their plate. This combination makes them resentful, irritable, and highly judgmental, as no one can live up to such a high standard of work. They also end up making more mistakes and experiencing diminished performance over time.

A young OB-GYN physician I know is a classic example of this. He is single and works about eighty hours per week. He brings in more income than anyone else in the group and his patients love him. He is a sincere and really good-hearted physician.

Early on, his partners were thrilled to have him on board, but that has changed over time. Because of his work-addicted, type-A tendencies, he is causing the staff around him to become disgruntled and burned out. Staff turnover has increased, and the extra income he brings to the group has a real financial ramification — the cost of staff replacement. In addition he has begun to take on risky cases that leave his partners feeling concerned. This will lead to lawsuits and future problems for the group. His partners are also concerned for his health. He is a heart attack waiting to happen.

Always in a Rush and Hyper-Busy
Workaholics tend to multitask heavily and often complain about how much they have to do. If they are not doing more than one thing at a time, they feel that they are slacking off. No one else is fast enough for them. They often over-schedule their time and are therefore chronically late.

No Time for Self-Care
It may seem obvious by now that workaholics cannot make make the necessary time in their schedules to take care of themselves. At least you're reading this!

Work Addiction Risk Test
There are multiple ways of defining work addiction. Bryan E. Robinson designed a very useful test (see *Chained to the Desk*, 52–54).

The following test was devised to help you evaluate yourself. Put the number that best fits you in each blank:

1 = never true, 2 = sometimes true, 3 = often true, 4 = always true
Total your score, and then look at the scale below.

_____1. I prefer to do things myself rather than ask for help.
_____2. I get impatient when I have to wait for someone else or when something takes too long.
_____3. I seem to be in a hurry and racing against the clock.
_____4. I get irritated when I'm interrupted while I'm in the middle of something.
_____5. I stay busy and keep many irons in the fire.
_____6. I find myself doing two or three things at once, such as eating and writing a memo while talking on the telephone.

_____7. I overcommit myself by biting off more than I can chew.

_____8. I feel guilty when I'm not working on something.

_____9. It's important that I see the concrete results of what I do.

_____10. I'm more interested in the final results of my work than in the process.

_____11. Things never seem to move fast enough or get done fast enough for me.

_____12. I lose my temper when things don't go my way or work out to suit me.

_____13. Others complain that, without realizing it, I ask the same question after I've already been given the answer.

_____14. I spend a lot of time planning and thinking about future events while tuning out the here and now.

_____15. I find myself continuing to work after my coworkers have finished.

_____16. I get angry when people don't meet my standards of perfection.

_____17. I get upset when I'm in situations where I cannot be in control.

_____18. I tend to put myself under pressure with self-imposed deadlines.

_____19. It's hard for me to relax when I'm not working.

_____20. I spend more time working than on socializing, hobbies, or leisure activities.

_____21. I dive into projects to get a head start before all the phases have been finalized.

_____22. I get upset with myself for making even the smallest mistake.

_____23. I put more thought, time, and energy into my work than I do into relationships with other people.

_____24. I forget, ignore, or minimize celebrations such as birthdays, reunions, anniversaries, or holidays.

_____25. I make important decisions before I have all the facts and have thought them through.

Scoring:

25–56 You are not work addicted.

57–66 You are mildly work addicted.

67–100 You are highly work addicted.

The Realities of Work Addiction
This material is adapted from Bryan E. Robinson's *Chained to the Desk.*

- Work addiction is a compulsive disorder that workaholics carry into the workplace. It is not created by the workplace.
- Work addiction is a mental-health problem, not a virtue, and it can create more problems than it can solve for the workplace.

- The superhero facade masks deeper emotional and adjustment problems that workaholics shield with their accomplishments.
- Workaholics do not sacrifice free time and family time for their work; they do it for ego gratification.
- Although most workaholics say that they enjoy their jobs, work satisfaction is not a prerequisite to work addiction.
- Workaholics become chemically addicted to their own adrenaline because of the stress they put themselves under, and they crave additional crises to maintain work highs.
- Work addiction can be a primary addiction or a secondary one that blends with other addictions.
- Workaholics do not have to be gainfully employed to become addicted; it can happen with any compulsive activity.
- Recovering balance after work addiction improves work quality and productivity, and helps workaholics become happier and more effective at what they do.
- Achieving balance from reduced work addiction requires more than cutting back on work hours; it involves deep personal introspection and insights, as well as attention to the parts of life that have been neglected.

More men are killed by overwork than the importance of the work justifies.

— Rudyard Kipling

Breaking the Cycle of Work Addiction

Let's start chipping away at your workaholic tendencies. The lower you scored on the test above, the fewer steps you need to take. There is always room for improvement.

Here are some simple steps to help reduce addiction to work:

1. Turn off your cell phone and pager when you don't need them on; you can't be that important!
2. When you are not on duty or call, stop being a doctor! If you struggle with this, chapter 15, " Psychosynthesis," will help.
3. Make sure you are home at a reasonable hour for dinner with your family at least four evenings per week.
4. Take one weekday off (if possible), four times yearly, to be irresponsible and unavailable. The world will not end without your input.
5. Take an evening or two a week to be with your loved ones, without the phone.
6. Make sure to take time for exercise four days per week.
7. Get a massage; you deserve it.

A Twelve-step Approach To Work Addiction
(Your First Tool Set)

A more rigorous way to manage workaholism would be to treat it as you would other addictions. You probably are thinking, "I deal with addicts regularly in my practice; why do I need to look at this?" While this is true, many of us don't know the twelve-step process, nor have we had personal experience with it. I encourage you to work the steps below and notice the changes that occur in your life. We all can use a bit of cleaning up, after all. This will also help you to understand what your addicted patients go through. Take a week to work the steps.

The twelve-step model, created by Bill W., the founder of Alcoholics Anonymous (A.A.), has been a highly successful model for abstaining from addictive behaviors. The process is accepting each step, one at a time, and then applying (working) it in your life . Ideally this should be done with the support of others. You might consider enrolling a friend or loved one as your twelve-step sponsor. It might be fruitful to work the steps with your colleagues as well.

While working the steps may seem a bit extreme, there is much to be learned from this tried and true model. After all, aren't lowering your chance of mortality and maintaining your family life worth a bit of hard personal work? There are also a few "lite" steps for those of you not yet ready to take the full plunge and for those who scored low on the work addiction test. Please adapt this in any way you find useful. For those of you who scored in the middle to high range on the work addiction test, "lite" may not be enough. For those of you who see workaholism and substance abuse as a substantial issue in your family, I would suggest attending Al Anon, CoDA, or A.A. meetings. This will help you grasp the deeper meaning of the twelve steps and codependency.

While only some of this may apply to your life today, it will help you to understand the treatment of addictive behaviors in a successful, psychosocial model. In this program, I've taken liberties with the language in order to fit it to workaholism, but the philosophy is intact. I've also substituted the term *higher power* for the word *God* used in the original text. The twelve steps have value, regardless of your religious beliefs.

The first pre-step is to find a sponsor. This can be a family member or friend. It is ideal if you and a friend are working the steps together. Think of your sponsor as your coach. This friend will help to keep you honest about going through the process. Accountability is critical for success!

The steps are as follows, adapted and modified from www.aa.org, the official Web site of A.A.:

STEP 1
We admit that we are powerless over excessive work, that our lives have become unmanageable. Work addiction is an addiction heavily coated with denial: "I have lots of friends and activities outside of work," or my favorite, "But

I love my work." This doesn't hold up to close scrutiny. Honesty is the key to success with the first step; denial is not allowed. Recovery can begin with one simple admission that we are powerless over workaholism. This call for honesty holds true for our friends and families as also, because they can facilitate either workaholism or recovery.

STEP 1 LITE
Accept that workaholism has been a part of our lives for a long time. We will need help in managing this behavior! Powerlessness is often a difficult concept for us control-freak doctors to accept. The serenity prayer is a great way to start. Post this on your mirror or desk and repeat it to yourself every morning and evening:

> *God, grant me the serenity to accept the things I cannot change,*
> *the courage to change the things I can, and the wisdom to know the difference.*

— Attributed to theologian Reinhold Niebuhr, circa 1934

STEP 2
We have come to believe that a power greater than ourselves can restore us to sanity. Faith is the key to this step. Before a higher power can begin to operate, we must first believe that it can. This step may require conversations with a religious leader, mentor, or spiritual guide.

STEP 2 LITE
It is important to believe that there are other ways of thinking than the ones we hold.

If this is true, someone or something out there might have a different path. For some of us, a higher power might be the love of our friends and families. They can surely help us regain our sanity!

STEP 3
We now make a decision to turn our wills and our lives over to the care of a higher power as we understand it. Surrender is the key to this step. A lifetime of self-will running riot can come to a screeching halt and change forever, by making a simple decision to turn it all over to a higher power.

STEP 3 LITE
We will ask for help and will surrender to a higher power. Surrender means acknowledging that the current situation is not working At times, seeing the big picture is all that is needed. When we focus on minutia, life gets out of hand. This is where our meditations will be most useful!

It is important to note that surrender is not submission. Submission is the place of a victim or failure; surrender and acceptance are freeing. Think of a time in your life when you were able to accept something for what it was or someone for who they truly were. This is pure surrender, the root of unconditional love.

STEP 4
We now make a searching and fearless moral inventory of ourselves. The beginning of healing must start and continue with soul searching. Recovery is a process of learning, awakening, and relearning. There is a saying in the twelve-step programs: "Recovery is a process, not an event."

STEP 4 LITE
Self-discovery is a wonderful and sometimes scary process. This program can be one piece of your self-discovery. There are many routes of self-discovery:
- Psychological approaches
- Marital and relationship evaluation
- Wilderness journeys
- Physical challenges such as training for a marathon
- Artwork
- Dance
- Men's and women's groups

STEP 5
We admit to the higher power, to ourselves, and to another human being the exact nature of our wrongs. Accepting our limitations and wrongdoings may be the most difficult step to take. Once we admit to our fallibility, growth can begin.

STEP 5 LITE
Spending time to evaluate what we do that is not effective and errors we have made, whether in work, relationships, or judgment, is a valuable process. How many life mistakes have we made because of our overwork? If we are brave enough, making a list can be helpful. Why do this? When we enumerate the issues, we can then begin to compensate for them.

STEP 6
We are entirely ready to have the higher power remove all of our defects of character. The key to this step is acceptance, accepting character defects exactly as they are and becoming entirely willing to let them go.

STEP 6 LITE
Can we love someone who is flawed? Can we love ourselves in the same way? This is a big challenge for us perfectionists! This means accepting and loving all of our positive and negative qualities.

Life is what happens when you're busy making other plans

— John Lennon

STEP 7

We humbly ask the higher power to remove our shortcomings. The spiritual focus of this step is humility, asking a higher power to do something that cannot be done by self-will or mere determination.

STEP 7 LITE

To some degree, our medical training perpetuates the myth that we can make life-or-death decisions. Give it up! As it is often said, "We write the prescriptions; God heals." Are we truly omnipotent? Let's admit it, we're not that good. We and our patients need the help of a higher power.

STEP 8

We now make a list of all persons we have harmed, and are becoming willing to make amends to them all. The harm we do may be subtle.

STEP 8 LITE

Think of ways in which you may have harmed your family or friends. This harm is unlikely to be intentional, but is no less real. Did you miss a child's activity for work? Did you ever pass on an opportunity to be with your significant other for work? Important: Don't presume that their silence means that they weren't hurt. Ask them! Whom have you hurt?

STEP 9

We make direct amends to such people whenever possible, except when to do so would injure them or others. Making amends may seem like a bitter pill to swallow, but for those serious about recovery it can be great medicine for the spirit and soul.

STEP 9 LITE

Making amends can be tough but also fun. Think of creative ways to make up for your lack of attention. Get romantic, be playful. Importantly, don't just "make up" once; be committed to change over time. A dozen roses won't make up for twenty years of neglect. It's going to take a bit of work. This, however, is where the fun begins. Making up to the people you love feels great, can really be creative, and is almost always welcome! Try to make at least one apology a week.

STEP 10

We continue to take personal inventory, and when we are wrong, promptly admit it. Nobody likes to admit to being wrong. We are human; we will make mistakes.

Growth and change take time. Give yourself that time, and when you reach an area of learning, don't stop your growth. Acknowledge it and continue to grow. This is an ongoing process.

STEP 11

We seek through prayer and meditation to improve our conscious contact with the higher power, praying only for knowledge of the higher power's will for us and for the power to carry it out. The purpose of this step is to discover the plan a higher power, as we understand it, has for our lives. While an answer may never come, the pursuit is the process.

STEP 11 LITE

Prayer, creativity, and loving intention are useful always. Remember, don't pray for what you want; rather, give thanks for what you already have. Stay aware and look for the larger plan. Meditation is a great way to do this.

STEP 12

Having had a spiritual awakening as the result of these steps, we now try to carry this message to workaholics and to practice these principles in all our affairs. For those in recovery programs, practicing this step is simply how it works.

STEP 12 LITE

Let's help our friends. We are often afraid to extend help to colleagues who are struggling, because we don't want them to know that we see their struggle. Remember, if we don't try to help, they will get worse. When we find ways that work for us, we can share them.

A.A. also has something called "The Twelve Traditions." These are a series of questions and philosophies meant to support the growth of the community in A.A. There is much wisdom in the following questions, and you may find it useful to answer them. Some may not directly apply to you, but the concepts are worth looking at for your personal growth. I have taken and modified some of the key questions from this area of the A.A. literature for your thought.

1. In my medical community, am I a healing, mending, integrating person, or am I divisive?
2. Am I a peacemaker? Or do I, with pious preludes such as, "just for the sake of discussion," plunge into argument?
3. Am I gentle with those who rub me the wrong way, or am I abrasive?
4. Do I make competitive remarks, such as comparing one student, resident, or physician with another?
5. Do I put down some medical activities as if I were superior for not participating in this or that aspect of my medical community?

6. Am I as considerate of other physicians as I want them to be of me?
7. Do I spout platitudes about love while indulging in and secretly justifying behavior that bristles with hostility?
8. Am I actively involved in my medical community?
9. Do I share with my fellow physicians all of myself, both the bad and the good, accepting as well as giving the help of fellowship?
10. In group discussions, do I have to save face, or can I yield in good spirit to the group conscience and work cheerfully along with it?
11. In group discussions, do I sound off about matters on which I have no experience and little knowledge?
12. In my mind, do I prejudge some of my colleagues as losers?
13. Is there some type of physician that I privately do not want in my medical community?
14. Do I set myself up as a judge of whether a newcomer is sincere or phony?
15. Am I overly impressed by stature? Can I simply treat all doctors as people trying to manage problems?
16. Do I put down other peoples' behaviors when they are different from mine, or do I learn from them?
17. Am I willing to help other physicians without regard to whom or what is in it for me?
18. In my medical community, do I try to sound like an expert on medicine? On sociology? On psychology? On spiritual matters? Or, heaven help me, even on humility?
19. Do I still try to boss other members of my medical community?
20. Do I resist formal aspects of my medical community because I fear them as authoritative?
21. Can I honestly share my own personal experience without giving the impression I am stating the absolute medical opinion?
22. Do I sometimes promote good health so fanatically that I make it seem unattractive?
23. Why is it a good idea for me to place the common welfare of all physicians in my community before my individual welfare? What would happen to me if my medical community as a whole disappeared?
24. Do I ever try to get my colleagues to conform to my standards, not their own?
25. What is the real importance of me among more than a million physicians?

CHAPTER 5 **Our Health**

Steve, the chairman of medicine at his hospital, is a forty-eight-year-old father of two. He is a dedicated father and husband. His goal in life was to achieve high status in the medical community. He has certainly accomplished this goal. To do so, he has published extensively, has worked seventy-hour weeks, and sleeps four to five hours per night. He tries to attend family events but often misses them. At times, he feels as if he has sacrificed his life for medicine. Although he has no family history of heart disease and has only marginal risk factors, Steve had a myocardial infarction (MI) at age forty-seven and a coronary-artery bypass graft (CABG) at age forty-eight.

Statistics on physician health are not readily available; however, a few studies have been done. In the early 1990s, studies showed that we smoked less, exercised more, and ate healthier than our patients; yet, our overall mortality was higher than any other professional group. Our per-capita rates of heart disease, depression, and stroke were higher than any other working group, and the lifespan of a physician was shorter than comparable socioeconomic groups. Most disturbing, though a bit dated, is that women physicians had a life expectancy ten years lower than the general population in the same socioeconomic category.[1,2]

I would like to comment on the issue of women physician mortality first, before my female readers run out to increase their life insurance. Keep in mind that this statistic is from 1991. The women who would have died by that time had gone to medical school, roughly, in the 1940s and 1950s. These women faced a difficult task, trying to be accepted in a completely male profession and a society that did not yet readily accept women as physicians. This has changed significantly with the majority of current medical school enrollees being women; however, even today, medicine is still a male-dominated profession and not always an easy place for women. In addition, women physicians still are expected to perform most of the housework and parenting roles, so while it's gotten easier for women, it's still far from ideal. Add to this the fact that most women physicians are perfectionists who are trying to do two jobs that are impossible to do perfectly (work and home). This is still a recipe for disaster.

While these data are a bit frightening, more recent data suggests that our overall mortality is improving, although not by much. We now live roughly five years longer than other professionals. The top ten causes of death for white, male physicians were essentially the same as those of the general population, although physicians were more likely to die from cerebrovascular disease, accidents, and suicide; but less likely to die from chronic obstructive pulmonary disease, pneumonia/influenza, or liver disease than were other professional white men.[3] When viewed from the perspective of our good-exercise, nonsmoking, self-care knowledge base and healthy eating, this doesn't appear to be a substantial gain. In addition the high rates of cerebrovascular disease, accidents, and suicide suggest a high-stress life.

Physician disability claims have increased 50 to 60 percent in the last ten years; this may be another indication of bad times to come. Many disability carriers are refusing to underwrite physicians (from the UNUM Life Insurance Company of Portland, Oregon). I wouldn't underwrite us either. Our incomes are high, we are looking for ways out of practice, and our health is declining.

Despite having better health than many, poor-health behaviors are substantial, even in early physician training, and poor-health behaviors worsen over time. One study evaluated a cross section of 512 medical students. The outcome measures were self-reported health behaviors and ratings of the importance of prevention. A linear decreasing trend was noted, with first-year students rating the importance of prevention the highest, and fourth-year students rating it the lowest. Additionally, this study attempted to correlate health behaviors with perceptions. The results show significant relationships between student-reported behaviors and corresponding perceptions. The authors went on to state, "...the attrition of interest in prevention during undergraduate medical training is cause for concern; future clinical practice will be strongly motivated by their perceptions." Medical students are learning how to be unhealthy and therefore become the worst possible teachers for their future patients.[4]

How can our health outcomes be less than stellar? We seem to be so healthy. While superficial health behaviors would predict a long and healthy life, our psychological profiles predict increased cardiovascular disease, unhappy marriages, and more suicides. Being anxious, overworked, under-rested, type-A, perfectionististic, judgmental, hostile, and depressed individuals is not in our best interest!

Emotional Health and Disease Risk

The relationship of emotional states to coronary artery disease (CAD) development and adverse outcomes is a growing area of interest in the cardiovascular literature. The emotional states linked to adverse cardiovascular outcomes and risk factors include depression, hostility, anxiety, anger, social isolation, hopelessness, life stress, and type-A personalities.[5]

Depression

Physicians have depression rates equal to or exceeding those of their patient population, with a greatly increased risk of suicidal mortality.[6] Depression is also highly correlated with adverse coronary outcomes. This relationship has been studied in individuals with known CAD without MI, post-MI, and also those at risk for but without diagnosed CAD. The correlation of increased depression with increased adverse cardiovascular events has been demonstrated in multiple age groups and in both men and women. The pathophysiology of this relationship is currently being researched, and multiple, logical pathways seem to be at play.

In most studies, depression is an independent predictor of increased mortality. This includes patients post-MI,[7, 8, 9] as well as those with diagnosed CAD without recent MI.[10–20] In one study, major depression is as predictive of post-MI mortality as left ventricular dysfunction.[7] In these studies, minor depression and depressive symptoms also increase cardiac event rates substantially. This effect is of a long-term duration and not just a transient effect of the acute event.[21] A recent study by Bush et al. of elderly patients, post-MI with reduced ejection fraction, showed that depressive symptoms, not generally considered clinically significant and below the level usually considered predictive of increased post-MI mortality, did contribute significantly to mortality rates.[22]

Type-A Behavior

As described in the preceding chapters, we have type-A tendencies early in life and these tendencies blossom in our quest of the medical profession. Type-A behavior has also been clearly correlated with increased risk and death rates from coronary disease. This is especially apparent in hostile type-A people (judgmental).[34, 35] Type-A behaviors include anxiety and hostility.

The Physiology of Anxiety, Type A, Hostility, and Depression

Multiple physiological pathways are linked with and altered by mental and emotional states. It is no longer reasonable to consider these states as separate from cardiovascular physiology and pathophysiology.

Corticosteroid Balance Corticosteroid balance is altered in individuals with depression, anxiety, and hostility.[24] These emotional states lead to increased production of corticotrophin-releasing factor and serum cortisol. Elevated cortisol levels increase blood pressure, although the mechanisms are unclear.[25] Elevated cortisol increases LDL cholesterol, VLDL production and mobilization by the liver, triglycerides (as a component of VLDL); and decreases HDL cholesterol.[26] Elevated cortisol increases serum amyloid A proteins, which are inflammatory to the endothelium and modify HDL function.[27] These mechanisms all contribute to atherogenesis.

Catecholamines Catecholamines are also increased during depression, anxiety, and hostility.[28] Catecholamines are associated with increased production and mobilization of LDL cholesterol and triglycerides, and decreases in HDL cholesterol. They also increase blood pressure and arrhythmic tendencies. All of these mechanisms are likely to be involved with the increased mortality and morbidity associated with depression and depressive symptoms. Catecholamines also alter platelet function, which may also be an underlying mechanism. Depressed individuals may also develop significant impairments in platelet function via other mechanisms, including enhanced platelet reactivity and release of platelet products such as platelet factor 4 and ß-thromboglobulin, which are pro-atherogenic.[29, 30]

There is also evidence that points to hypercoagulability in depression. In patients with atherosclerosis and impaired endothelial anticoagulant function, procoagulant responses to acute stressors may outweigh anticoagulant mechanisms and thereby promote a hypercoagulable state.[31] This may contribute to micro-thrombosis and atherogenesis.

Heart Rate Variability (HRV) HRV is an indicator of autonomic function, and another likely link between adverse cardiac events and depression, anxiety, and hostility. Low HRV is associated with high sympathetic tone. High sympathetic tone is associated with increased arrhythmias, vasoreactivity, hyper-coagulabilty, and thrombosis.[28] Low HRV patterning is associated with higher risk of sudden death and MI in patients with CAD,[32–36] although it is not clear if this is a cause or effect relationship.

Low HRV is also found in individuals with CAD, who are depressed when compared with those who are not depressed. In the Carney et al. study of individuals post-MI, those who were depressed (major and minor) had low HRV compared to those who were not depressed. HRV was equally low in those who had major or minor depression or dysthymia, when compared to those without depressive symptoms.[33] Low HRV is also associated with anxiety and may be a trigger to arrhythmias.[36]

Social Isolation
Multiple studies have linked social isolation to coronary disease and all cause mortality.[37–46] Although we often act as social butterflies, physicians, as discussed in the previous chapter, tend toward isolationism, or social withdrawal, and a strong need for control. We do not allow ourselves to be vulnerable, because we are afraid of appearing imperfect (which we are). This also decreases the likelihood of deep interpersonal contact. The physiology of this phenomenon has been marginally studied, but observational data is strong indicating enhanced risk of suicide, mental illness, malignant tumor, hypertension, and CAD.[47]

Taking care of your emotional well-being is as important as taking care of your physical well being!

CHAPTER 6 Stress and Burnout

Sherry is a forty-three-year-old physician employee of a community clinic. She is the mother of two children, aged ten and twelve. She prides herself on being a very good physician and mother. However, she does feel that it is tougher each day to go to work, and finds that her "fuse" is growing shorter and shorter. She also has more generalized fatigue and headaches more frequently.

For the typical physician, stress results from external events and how we manage them. How we manage stress is often dictated by our personality structure. As we proceed in the process of becoming physicians, we are placed under ever-increasing performance stresses. I would like to show you how such stresses build over time without our complete awareness.

The graph below was taken from a World War II study. The goal of the study was to evaluate the effect of stress on performance in battle. Soldiers new to the battlefield were followed and evaluated on their performance. As you can see, the initial adjustment and learning period was roughly fifteen days. During this time, soldiers were on the steep learning curve, becoming more efficient, learning what needed to be done, observing errors, and improving their function. This led to a period of maximum efficiency over the next ten to fifteen days. At this stage, they knew what was needed, and functioned at peak capacity with few errors. After the thirtieth day in battle, the soldiers were found to be less efficient, making more errors. Surprisingly they were not aware of these errors. This was because they had already achieved maximal efficiency and there was nothing else to learn. Once achieving the peak level of function, they believed that they operated at such a high level at all times.

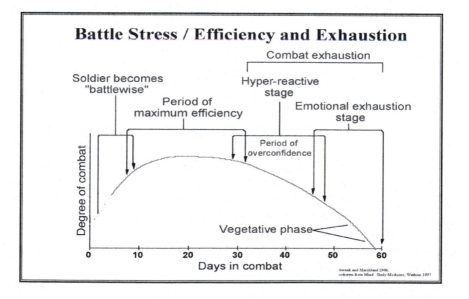

Battle Stress / Efficiency and Exhaustion

I find the period of overconfidence to be most intriguing. The soldiers believed they were operating maximally, but they were making more and more mistakes as the days progressed. The genesis of these errors was fatigue. In our lives as physicians, we know most of what we need to know (therefore, a tendency toward overconfidence), yet we make mistakes regularly. This too is due to fatigue. Keep in mind that fatigue is the number-one cause of medical error.

Who notices that you are in this state of increasing fatigue, and why won't they tell you about it? The first to notice would be your spouse and family members. They are reluctant to tell you because you are might offer a defensive response. They also are trying to protect you with their belief that if they tell you, it will make you feel worse.

Your colleagues will also recognize your fatigue. They probably won't tell you about it for the same reasons as your family (fear of your defensiveness and making it worse). In addition, they, too, are probably experiencing fatigue, and verbalizing it for you forces them to look at themselves (not pretty). Lastly, if they are your work partners, they fear that telling you will inspire you to take time off. Then they will have more work to do.

Even your patients will see that you are tired. Most patients won't tell you because they have a delusion to maintain, that you are the best doctor for them. Admitting to themselves that you are toast would burst that bubble for them. Occasionally patients who have a long-term relationship with you will tell you that you are in trouble. A colleague once told me that he had not had a vacation in over three years. He planned to take a month off but cancelled last minute due to call schedules. Upon seeing him in the office, his patient reminded him that he was supposed to be away, and said "Doc, you need a vacation!"

You are the only one who can answer the question, "How am I doing?" and be honest about it. If the answer is "not good," then only you can choose to change the situation.

The Road to Burnout

Let's have a look at how most physicians get to the state of burnout. Before college, life is generally stress free for us in the areas of performance. The only pressures that exist are internal ones such as perfectionism, which, as discussed earlier, can be driven by our parents, our mentors, or our competitive nature. We usually easily accomplished the tasks of grade school and high school. We were top in our classes and generally functioned, adapted, and performed very well. When given a challenge we rose to it with little hesitancy. Our performance of these tasks exceeded the expectations of our teachers and parents. At this time in our lives, we were happy and enjoyed learning, playing, and also our quiet time. Most of us remember these years fondly.

In college we continued to rise to challenges, by learning to flex and adapt to changes and challenges readily, while leaving room for fun things in our lives. There were other students of varied interests around, which helped us stay connected to activities outside of our chosen area of study.

However, for most of us, it was at this point when focusing on a goal became a predominant behavior. The goal was medical school. Because it was admirable to most of the people in our lives, this goal allowed us to eliminate things we didn't want to do and forced us to let go of some things that we wanted to do (thus, enhancing work-addiction behaviors). Because of our single-mindedness and ability to perform, we rose again to the top of the heap. In the process, we learned a new, useful tool, hyper-focus. Hyper-focus allowed us to keep our eye on the prize (medical school) and to eliminate a great deal of fun, social events, and other healthful behaviors. Here, we became masters of delayed gratification. This was a bit monocular at times and disallowed us the ability to see the big picture. After all, we had a goal!

It is important to note that, at that time, most of us still had good boundaries and understood our capacities. We knew what we could do and what we needed to do, and were able to focus on the task at hand. We were not overly fatigued and rarely, if ever, blamed others when things did not go well.

Medical school required a very high level of discipline and energy. We began to eliminate or downplay parts of our lives that were unrelated to school. Hyper-focus was in full gear and necessary for success. We pushed ourselves maximally and decreased our sleep. The parts of our lives unrelated to our career began to suffer. Unfortunately, one of those parts was basic self-care including nutrition, exercise, and sleep. A study of medical student health behaviors demonstrates this well. Over the four years of medical school, the outcome measures were the students' own health behaviors and perceptions of the importance of preventive health behaviors for patients. This study demonstrated a decline in exercise, sleep, and nutritional quality. With this decline, there was a linear relationship to the student's own perception of the importance of preventive health for the patient.[1] This is documentation of the decline in our well-being. At some level, we believe that we can put our own health on hold while learning to help others. There also must be an underlying belief that we will get back to self-care in residency while starting a practice and while having families.

This mind-set sounds absurd, doesn't it? This is the ultimate in codependent behavior; our fear of failure and displeasing others (including ourselves) outweighs not only our own health needs but that of our patients, as in the above study. What a ridiculous behavior to adapt! The decline in our belief in prevention also proves that those who can't do, can't teach!

Returning to the analogy of the World War II soldier, we are now at maximal efficiency.

We are pushing ourselves at top speed, getting just enough sleep to survive and using more stimulants, such as caffeine. We squeeze in extra work to compensate for fatigue. Do you remember staying awake late the night before an exam to review your notes, knowing that sleep may be more important for your focus, but being unable to sleep because you were hyper-driven?

It is also at this point when our relationships begin to suffer. We put off family and personal needs using schoolwork as the excuse. While this may have been functional during college, it is a terrible habit to develop. We also start losing good boundaries about what we can and can't do, which is fatigue related. Lastly, we internalize our stress, which is often experienced as depression and fatigue.

Medical school may be the first place where we hit this early fatigue state. We are likely to hit this place over and over in our working lives. The pre-burnout stage is a place where many of us live day to day. It feels as if we are just getting by, but if one more thing happened, we would be thrown into overload. The symptom complex is as follows:

- Reading a journal article over and over until you realize that you are just too tired to absorb the information
- Staying in the office late to do charts and at some point realizing that you are being ineffective because you are tired
- Mild to modest depression
- Irritation with patients
- Knowing that you are not spending enough time with family and friends
- Missing your hobbies or fun events in life
- Dreaming about work
- Taking the first three days of vacation to stop your busy, multitasking brain

If any of this sounds familiar, it's time to start reconfiguring your life before you burn out. Warning signs are a blessing!

Burnout

Burnout occurs for most of us, and can happen during or after training. It can be transient, lasting for days or months, or it can be a long-term state. Most of us don't realize when it's happening. The proportion of doctors showing above-threshold levels of stress has stayed remarkably constant at around 28 percent, whether the studies are cross-sectional or longitudinal, compared with around 18 percent in the general working population.[2]

For people accustomed to functioning at high levels of energy, burnout can often be experienced as depression. The rates of depression and suicide among physicians are higher than the general population.[3]

As discussed above, the first people to recognize our burnout are those closest to us, such as our families and friends. This creates a dilemma for them. They see that we are burned out. They know we are working above capacity, and they don't want to remind us of this. They are afraid, at best, that they would be telling us something that we couldn't do anything about, or, at worst, that we might blast them for reminding us. It is no wonder that they are reluctant to say anything to us. This is another form of codependency. Their lack of action facilitates your decline. Ask them honestly whether you are burned out, be ready to hear the answer without blasting, and then ask them for help.

What is the burnout symptom complex? The first signs of burnout are that everything we have been holding inside starts to leak out. We lose perspective of the big picture and begin to blame and judge others harshly. The common language is, "If it weren't for ___, this wouldn't have happened," or we might find ourselves complaining about the same person on nearly a daily basis without actually managing the situation. We begin to externalize our frustrations and feel bad about our behavior; we yell at people and then get depressed or upset with ourselves for losing it. If we don't externalize our feelings we become significantly depressed.

It is at this time when our type-A tendencies are running at max. We are multitasking so much that we start forgetting what we have already done. We begin to misplace things, and then blame others for misplacing our things. We run late for everything. We also become hyperirritable. Small things that didn't used to upset us now start to eat at us. These include issues in our relationships, so our personal lives begin to crash.

We have now hit survival mode, where we can only respond to immediate issues. Planning and forethought just take too much energy, so we shut down emotionally and go on automatic pilot. We lose all creativity, and knee-jerk reactions become the mode of being.

As you can see, each stage of our regression brings us closer to living in a reflexive, midbrain, reactive state. This is a learned survival behavior. In this mode we desire to do the least possible thing we can do in response to given external circumstances. For example, if someone is bothering us, it takes less time and effort to say "bug off" than it would to try to resolve the issues at hand. This does not serve the relationship and generally creates more trouble for us and them. If you find yourself blaming others for your unhappiness, watch out!

CHAPTER 7 **The Road Within**

*People travel to wonder at the height of the mountains, at the huge
waves of the seas, at the long course of the rivers, at the vast
compass of the ocean, at the circular motion of the stars, and yet
they pass by themselves without wondering.*

— St. Augustine, 354–430 AD

In the past chapters of this book we have looked at our stress, our tendency to burn out, our personalities, and some of the external stresses in the system of medicine. It is now time to begin the process of finding out where we wish to go. The first step in this process is to look within.

The road to balance starts with self-understanding and analysis. How much does your personality contribute to your stress? How can you begin to modify your behaviors and responses? There are many paths to this place of understanding. Over the next few sections, we will explore some of these paths such as psychosynthesis, meditation, and HeartMath techniques. All of these will serve as tools toward greater growth. I have chosen these tools for you because they were most helpful to me in my growth, creativity, and performance.

Self-Evaluation

This is the first tool in your tool kit, the ability to evaluate yourself honestly. It is a restructuring tool to be used as a prelude to change. Give yourself a half hour to do this work.

Who are you?

When you meet someone, how do you define yourself? By your work, your relationships with others, or what you enjoy doing? Most likely it depends on where you are at the time and what the situation calls for. If you are in a medical meeting you will introduce yourself as "Doctor Jones," whereas at a party you may be "Sally Jones." The way we define ourselves sets the tone for the subsequent interaction. Our self-definition also determines our current behaviors. "Dr. Jones" may be thoughtful, reserved, and possibly a bit judgmental, while "Sally Jones" is fun and playful, and loves to dance.

Think of all the roles you play in the course of a few days or weeks: mother, father, child, parent, teacher, gardener, athlete, lover, or lazy bum; the list may be endless. Each personality is a separate, but related, way of being, with its own complexity and nature. What if you then add mood states on top of this? The angry lover, the jealous lover, the passionate lover — the list gets longer, and yet they are all you.

The first step within is to begin to understand and "own" each of those parts of you. They all are you, even the angry or intolerant parts. If you don't "own" them, you can't manage them. This, then, allows you to choose who you want to be at any given moment, and puts you back in charge of your emotions. You may try to list these different parts of yourself to fully understand your own depth. Take some blank paper and make a list of all the different versions of "you" there are. Use the following categories:

1. Activities (doctor, soccer mom)
2. Moods (angry one, lover)
3. Relationship roles (mom, dad, son, daughter)

List as many as you possibly can. It's fun to do this with your spouse, a friend, or your children. They may know some parts of you that you are unaware of.

Another fun way to do this is to sit with a partner and look into each other's face. Take turns asking each other, "Who are you?" and see what answers arise. In doing this, you'll be able to go deeper into understanding yourself and your partner than by just doing it alone.

Evaluate Your Expectations

Evaluating your expectations of others and considering shifting them will be a big part of managing your stress. A majority of our frustrations and anger come from our expectations of others not being met. You may hold expectations for your staff or your children and then get angry when they don't perform to those expectations. This is especially true for perfectionists who project their own high self-standards onto others. Have you ever said to your child, "Why don't you understand the math? It's so easy." This does not promote learning. It only belittles the child.

Our expectations are pervasive and a major cause of stress. We expect people to drive courteously and be prompt, we expect our staffs to get it right, and we expect our spouses to be affectionate. If you find yourself getting angry at others because of your expectations, it may be time to consider whether your expectations are realistic. I don't want to suggest that inappropriate behaviors or bad performance should be acceptable, but if you spill a significant amount of catecholamines with anger at others because they don't live up to your level or performance, your bar may be too high.

Another way our expectations can hurt us is with our inability to change them as the world changes. Many physicians I know complain, "Medicine wasn't supposed to be this way" or "My patients were supposed to listen to me." Again the key is to ask yourself, Is this realistic in today's world?

Expectations are rules made up by society, our families, or us. You weren't born knowing these rules to be truths, so they should always be open to interpretation and reinterpretation.

Everything can be taken from a man but one thing: the last of the human freedoms — to choose one's attitude in any given set of circumstances.

— Victor Frankel

Evaluate Your Influences

Who influenced your career choices? Was it your parents who pushed or inspired you, great physicians who served as role models, or was it religious or spiritual leaders or maybe a great author who inspired you? Make a brief list of these important people. Generating gratitude is extremely important (possibly the strongest power tool of all).

Often, some of our greatest influences served us well at specific time of life. There is a popular saying: "When the student is ready, the teacher appears." We also may grow or change our desires, so that the life of the person we wanted to be when we grew up is no longer desirable.

As mentioned previously, my mentor in medical school was loved by his patients and his fellow faculty members. He was politically and scientifically active in his field of medicine, and as a teacher, he was without equal. He was there for us as students and as people. Even today his wise advice resonates in my head (almost twenty years later). He had incredible integrity, honesty and sincere empathy at all hours. He truly was what I wanted to be when I completed my training.

Twenty years later, I look back at that wonderful man and know that, had I become him, I probably would have lost or damaged my marriage along the way, and would not know my children as I know them today. However, many of my mentor's personal attributes are still relevant to me and I hope that I've successfully adopted them. I no longer want to be him "when I grow up"; I want to be me, with some of his qualities thrown into the mix.

An important way to manage stress is to be willing to release the influence of those who inspired you if that influence is no longer relevant to you today. Take a moment to appreciate those whom you have learned from. Don't forget the lessons, good or bad.

One way to evaluate what is important to you today is to list the attributes of people you admire. They may be people you know or they may be idealized versions of people. This will help you to identify the core attribute that you want to enhance in yourself. As you do this, notice that some attributes are efficient, such as "organized," while some are emotional or heart based, such as "caring" or "trusting."

Through this process you will see that it's the combination of the head and heart, or thinking and emotional, that we admire most. This is what is known as emotional intelligence, the true use of the head and heart in leadership and relationships.

Caring + Efficiency = Effectiveness
This equation is a key learning of the process developed by HeartMath LLC for business development seminars. We spend a great deal of our time searching for efficiencies, meaning how to do more in less time. This search often distracts from effectiveness. Effectiveness can be defined as achieving the greatest desired outcome with the lowest possible expenditure of energy. The biggest bang for your buck.

Effectiveness involves efficiency, but does not depend on efficiency alone. Have you ever known physicians who were highly efficient? Maybe they saw more patients in an hour than you could or did more procedures in a day than you could, but were they effective? How were their outcomes? Did they enjoy themselves? Did their patients love them? Did their coworkers respect them? Were they happy?

Being effective means having good outcomes, caring for your patients, being cared for by your patients, earning the respect of your coworkers, and connecting with those around you. This is not always the most efficient way of being (although it can be), but it is clearly the most effective.

Effectiveness involves heart. It involves showing care, consideration, love, and humor. It involves listening, empathizing, and understanding. These are traits that most physicians possess. We are generally caring people who want to do the right thing, however we define that. Being effective involves remembering to care rather than substitute efficiency for caring in the belief that the outcomes will improve. It is better to do right for one patient than to do wrong for ten!

One of the best ways to enhance our caring is to pay attention and understand what motivates us. What are our values? Have you ever done work of great meaning to you? Maybe this was volunteer work for a charity or great cause. Do you remember how you felt that evening, even if you worked for twelve hours? When we do work that is of value, it enhances our energy.

Caring + Value = Energy
Could you use a little more energy in your day? One of the best ways to do this is to add to your day work that is of value and meaning. In this way you enhance caring, effectiveness, and your own energy level, all of which are positive attributes in a medical career. Not bad work, if you can get it!

CHAPTER 8 What Makes a Happy Doc Happy?

For physician managers and organizations, What makes a doctor happy? may be the be-all and end-all question, yet the answer is very simple: physicians are happy when their work is challenging, promotes individual growth and expression, and allows them to make a difference in other peoples' lives. The need for these work-fulfillment characteristics has been shown to be true in the airline industry, service sector, and retail environments, which are often ahead of medicine in many aspects of client relationships and valuing the employee.[1]

Physicians are also happiest when their work, home, community, and spiritual lives are in balance.[2, 3] Physicians, especially women physicians, are also very dependent on the quality of interpersonal relationships at work. When relationships with staff, colleagues, and patients are going well, physicians can manage greater amounts of work pressure and stress. Physicians also are happiest when they have a sense of autonomy.[4] In part, this explains why many physicians are stressed as employees or when working in a managed-care setting.

Reasonable equity for our work is also very important to us. When we look at the concept of work-related equity, it falls into three categories: intrinsic, financial, and recognition equity.[3] While financial and recognition equity are easy to understand, intrinsic equity may not be so clear.

Intrinsic value or equity is composed of a sense of personal contribution, growth, responsibility, and achievement in your work. In this case achievement is as judged by the individual, not the system. Achievement can be great clinical outcomes, happy patients or staff, a clean desk, or a sense of learning and growth. In addition a key intrinsic value is the nature of the work itself.[5] Do you enjoy what you are doing each day?

How do you get people to do good work? Give them good work to do.

— Richard Gunderman, MD

When organizations are looking for ways to enhance worker satisfaction they often turn to extrinsic factors as opposed to intrinsic factors. Extrinsic factors include administrative policies or issues, salary, chain of command issues, the physical aspects of the workplace, and even our work schedules. When these factors are not adequate or functional, they become the focus of the physician's (or any worker's) attention and complaints. When they are adequate, people don't pay attention to them, and enhancing them only brings short-term attitudinal improvements. For example, if you were to get a raise or a new office when you already have adequate salary or a reasonable office, your mood would improve for about one month. However, the enhancement of the intrinsic factors will bring long-term attitudinal and even performance changes. Fredrick Herzberg likens efforts to enhance extrinsic factors to recharging an employee's batteries, while enhancing intrinsic factors is like installing a generator in an employee.[5]

Physician satisfaction is a key element of a successful health system. When physicians are happy, patients are happier with their visits, their outcomes, and the quality of the care they receive.[6] The patients of happier physicians have greater confidence and trust in their physician,[7] and the better long-term adherence to the recommended therapies.[8] This effect also enhances or diminishes patients' satisfaction, trust, and longevity with their health plan.[7]

Physician satisfaction also impacts physician longevity in academic and nonacademic work environments.[9, 10] Low satisfaction and high turnover lead to further stress and dissatisfaction on the part of the remaining physicians, as well as increased illness in the remaining workforce, thus creating a downward spiraling effect in the workplace.[8]

An additional stress on the system is the cost to replace a physician. In time, recruitment, and training, it costs at least one year of a physician's salary to replace a physician.[11] Over time, physician dissatisfaction becomes of critical importance to the health care system.

Enhancing the Intrinsic Values of Work and Life
(A Restructuring Tool — Fifteen Minutes)

Because the intrinsic factors are the key to work satisfaction and all else falls into place from there, let's begin to look at a way to enhance intrinsic values in your work. First on the list is the nature of the work itself. Do you enjoy what you do? Are you spending more of your time doing what you enjoy rather than what you don't enjoy?

I encourage you to do the following exercise: make a list of the activities in the course of a week that occupy the majority of your time. Identify each activity in the following order of levels from 1 to 4:

1. I am good at this activity and I enjoy doing this.
2. I am not good at this activity but want to learn how to do it or do it better.
3. I am good at this activity but don't enjoy doing it.
4. I am not good at this activity and don't care to learn how to do it better.

These levels are directly related to your intrinsic values and balance needs. If you are good at something (level 1), this activity fits the need for achievement and is work you enjoy, which energizes you. If you are not good at something but want to learn, or improve on, it (level 2), this activity meets the intrinsic values of personal growth, responsibility, and achievement. If you wish to enhance the value of your life, begin to enhance level 1 and 2 activities, and diminish level 3 or 4 activities.

Why do we take on too many level 3 activities? The trap for most physicians is that we are good at many different types of activities, and therefore are asked to do all kinds of things in our work or personal lives. We also tend to be people pleasers and aren't good at saying no to others. Using this, others will trap us with our egos: "You are so good at this" or "No one could do it better." If your plate is too full, it is healthier to politely say no to level 3 and 4 activities.

This simple model will also help you as an employer. With each employee, figure out (or ask them) what are their level 1 to 4 activities at work. By identifying them clearly, you can parcel out the work in the office in a way that enhances efficiency and satisfaction.

Ideally we would all be doing level 1 and 2 activities all day, every day; however, this is an unrealistic expectation. There will always be level 3 and 4 activities that you will need to do; just try to minimize them for yourself and your staff as much as possible.

One activity where this is particularly relevant is housecleaning. As more and more women are working full-time, one key activity that falls through the cracks is housecleaning. While most people want a clean home, women tend to be more agitated than men by a messy environment. In addition, a clean home increases a woman's sense of control and decreases her stress.[13] So why is the average woman physician reluctant to get a housekeeper? She feels like a failure if she can't do it herself. This is based in the female physician's model of what a perfect superwoman doc can do. She also tends to have a high need for control and a housekeeper won't do it the way she wants it done. This is type-A perfectionistic thinking; give it up already!

Joy

The concept of finding joy in your work may seem a bit abstract, New Agey, or unrealistic, but when you look at what motivates and drives people to greater performance, energy, and quality outcomes, joy is high on the list. If joy is too grandiose a word for you to describe work pleasure, think of accomplishment, success, a sense of well-being, or gratitude. Joy will include the intrinsic values of personal contribution, growth, a sense of responsibility, and achievement. Especially in medicine joy also includes the idea of serving others.

Do you experience joy in your work? What are the things at work that bring you joy? It might be when patients or their families thank you; this validates not only the work you did but also who you are as a person. It might be the joy of finding a new way of managing the office, schedule, or charts. It might be the simple and unusual joy of emptying the chart rack. It might be a sense of appreciation of your skills or for having a really enjoyable patient in your practice. Any of these things can give you fulfillment.

Joy also comes from serving others. Whom do you serve with your work, your patients, your colleagues, and your staff? You also serve your family through your work. The income you generate buys them a place to live, tuition, food, and fun things too.

However, income itself can be a trap. There is a simple story of a man in a suit approaching a fisherman on a dock. The man in the suit says to the fisherman, "If you invested in a boat, you could catch more fish. And if you caught more fish you could hire others to fish for you and maybe even afford many boats." The fisherman asks, "What would that get me?" The man in the suit replies, "This would vastly increase your income and give you more time for leisure activity." The fisherman responds sarcastically, "Well gee, Mister, then I could afford to sit on this dock and fish, which is what I love to do!" The lesson here is that money is a goal, not the goal. Joy comes from other sources.

Sometimes achieving joy means less income. My wife works at a community clinic for the underserved. Much of her joy comes from doing the work of service rather than being in a private practice where her income may be higher. Another joy here is that there are specialists who give up one or two days per month to see patients at the clinic for free. Essentially this costs them money, but what they gain back in satisfaction is far more valuable.

It is important to note that you are already doing work of value, even in the busiest day. Close you eyes, take a deep breath, and think of those you have helped and those who bring you joy in your day. Let your mind wander from person to person, from situation to situation. Experience how it feels in your body when you think of these people and moments. A brief excursion like this can bring you energy, even on those busy days.

Exercise — Joy
(Ten-Minute Power Tool)

As we search for energy and values, it is important to address what is already working for us. Take a moment to write the answers to the following questions.

1. Do you experience joy in your work?
2. What gives you pleasure at work?
3. Do others experience joy as a result of your work?
4. If so, list some of those who have experienced joy from your work.

Core Values
(A Maintenance Power Tool — Ten Minutes)

Underneath the intrinsic values lie your core values. These are the things that are most important to you in your life. For most of us the list might include family, friends, health, God, honesty, integrity, and many others. It also might include adventure, fun, and playfulness. I encourage you to create your own list and also ask your family to make up their own lists.

There is one basic rule that I have never seen broken: when we do work that supports our core values, it is energizing. When our work goes against our core values, it is energy draining. If your work goes against your core values, you are in the wrong job.

CHAPTER 9 **Managing Stress**

If we are to manage stress, we need to first define it. Stress is the automatic nonspecific response of the human organism to any change or demand. This means that we don't think whether or not we are stressed while the stress is occurring. The stress response is not a cortical one, but more limbic or midbrain based.

Stress is a particular relationship between a person and the environment that the person appraises as taxing or exceeding the individual's resources and endangering the person's well-being. This can be a pickup truck coming at you at sixty miles per hour or a work challenge that you don't feel ready for. The stress response is mediated by the autonomic nervous system.

There are two levels of stress: acute and chronic. Acute stress is when the threat is immediate and the need to respond is instantaneous. This is generally catecholamine mediated. Chronic stress, on the other hand, is when the threat is prolonged and unabated, and it usually involves the presence of cortisol in the blood.

It is important to remember that a stress response to a painful stimulus (e.g., a stubbed toe or sitting on a sharp object) is reflexive and not learned, whereas a perspective-related stress response is a learned response. You were not born knowing that failing an exam was bad or that your child not coming home on time was stressful. These are things that you learned, created, or adopted. With that in mind, managing stress can be looked at as creating a new response to a given learned circumstance, or midbrain reeducation. It would include, but not be limited to, the following: shifting perspective, emotional management, setting appropriate boundaries, learning what is controllable, or raising your stress threshold. Ways of doing this can include reconnecting with your life purpose, finding help through friends or a therapist, meditation, prayer, yoga, biofeedback, exercise, and hobbies. There are many other choices in addition to these few. All of these stress management techniques will help you to lower catecholamines and cortisol, and enhance cortical function.

As you now understand from reading the preceding chapters, the stress response is triggered by multiple sources: stress at work and home, and then our perception of the stressors as filtered through our personalities and attitudes. It is because of this that there are many ways of managing stress.

One way to manage stress is to eliminate the cause(s). Sometimes this is very manageable; for example, if you live in an apartment that has a difficult landlord, you can choose to stay there and be aggravated, wait until your lease ends and then move, or immediately break your lease and leave. Sometimes the choices may be more difficult. I was involved in a research project using intensive lifestyle change for heart patients; in this project there was a fifty-five-year-old man with a low ejection fraction and coronary ischemia who frequently fell asleep during the program sessions. The first thought was that he was either overmedicated or under-perfusing his brain. On evaluation and interview, it was discovered that he was working two jobs trying to pay for a very large mortgage. It became clear that, if he continued to live this way, he would likely be dead within a short period of time. In this case the decision to sell his house and downsize his life became the obvious choice, even though he struggled with the decision.

Other stresses may not have immediate or obvious remedies. For example, many of you are probably dealing with aging parents, some of whom may have significant health or financial problems. This type of situation can significantly complicate your life, and while it may be manageable, it is impossible to eliminate.

It is in these moments that shifting perspective of the stressor is useful. Simply put, this is seeing the stressor from a different vantage point. In the example above, being grateful that you have parents or have had good relationships with them is a perspective shift that helps to ease the stress. Knowing that you can serve them in their older years may help decrease the stress. None of this eliminates the cause of stress, but it will change the effect that the stress has on you.

You can apply perspective shifting to more short-term stress as well. If you recently had a fight with your spouse and are now stuck in the office, you can choose to run and rerun the argument in your head, which distracts you from your patient or staff. This usually will not lead to resolution of the argument, thus making you an ineffective and distracted physician and work partner. Another option would be to perform a simple perspective shift, remembering that you love your spouse and he or she loves you, and that there will be an opportunity to deal with the problem in the near future. This change of perspective allows you to focus on the task at hand and know that you have good intention to manage the "home front" with caring.

CHAPTER 10 A Cognitive Approach to Perspective Shifting

This is a restructuring power tool. Give yourself a few days to incorporate this content and to try the tools. The more you use this one, the stronger it gets!

As described in the preceding chapter, shifting perspective is one of the most useful ways to manage stress. Cognitive behavioral therapists describe practical, rational ways of shifting your thought processes using your thoughts. These are simple, yet powerful, perspective shifting tools. They help you identify ways of thinking that add stress and they help you to find a new way of thinking about the issue. In his book, *The Feeling Good Handbook,* David Burns, MD,[1] describes some of these "mistakes in thinking" and how to manage them. They are mistakes in that they increase stress, don't resolve problems, and can actually create problems for you.

The first step to modify a way of thinking is to recognize where you make these mistakes. Often the recognition of the mistake is enough to create the shift.

Perfectionism

As discussed earlier in the book, perfectionism is a very common and dramatic version of one of these mistakes in thinking. In the life of the perfectionist, it shows up in various ways. Most dramatically, it is a black and white way of looking at success and failure. As a perfectionist, if an outcome or situation falls short of your expectations, you see it as complete failure. This is usually a result of childhood conditioning, as described in chapter 4, "The Physician Personality." This is amplified in medical training when you are chastised for mistakes and not congratulated for partial successes.

In thinking about a situation, the true perfectionist only thinks of the flaw in the event and thus is frustrated and unsatisfied. For example, you've agreed to do a grand rounds presentation and spend many hours or days preparing to get it right. You go through the literature in great depth, because you want to educate your colleagues and do a good job overall. On the day of the presentation, you feel anxious but prepared. In the middle of the presentation, a colleague points out that one of your slides is outdated because just last week there was a study in the *New England Journal of Medicine* countering the very point you just made.

The perfectionist response to this would be twofold: On first glance you would be mad at your colleague for publicly identifying a flaw in your content, thus shaming you (not an uncommon event among a group of hyper-perfectionistic, competitive people). After the talk, the perfectionist's inner monologue might be, "I never should have agreed to do that talk" or "They don't appreciate how much time I put into this." The true perfectionist would think such things even if ten colleagues told them that the talk was great and they got a lot out of it. So where does this lead the perfectionist? It leaves him or her feeling dissatisfied, unhappy, and angry.

What would be a healthy, low-catecholamine response to this circumstance? To enjoy the congratulations of your colleagues, to appreciate the colleague who questioned your slide, and to make that into a discussion during your talk. Additionally, appreciate yourself for your hard work, and know that now you have a great talk "in the pocket" to be used again. After all, 99 percent good should be good enough for anyone.

A more subtle, yet often more pervasive, version of perfectionist thinking is described by David Burns as applying a mental filter.1 This is the tendency to dwell on a single negative detail or occurrence that happened in the past. For example, you run into a colleague early in the day and, in passing, say something that you later realize may have been offensive. This thought continues to creep back into your head throughout the day. You keep thinking you should call your colleague, but never find the time or may be too embarrassed to do so. As you proceed through your day, this thought becomes a minor obsession and distracts you from thinking clearly. It begins to affect your mood and even your functionality a bit. This negative attitude based on a previous event is a mental filter that colors all other events of the day.

This is a very common distortion in thinking for perfectionists. They cannot accept a flawed moment. This is a slightly "gray" version of "all or nothing" thinking, which is more black and white. Perfectionism is rampant in medicine. Is this you? Could you imagine not dwelling on the negative for five minutes? Could you believe that this voice in your head telling you that you made a mistake may not be correct? How long will you let this go on? Will you lie in bed tonight thinking about it and feeling agitated?

What is a healthy response? Call the person and apologize for what you said, and then let it go. Under most circumstances the person will be happy and thankful that you called. It is also likely that your friend or colleague has completely forgotten about the incident by now and will tell you so. Learning this will substantially lower your catecholamines and improve your mood.

Another problem is that the perfectionist does not derive the normal pleasure from positive outcomes or tasks. True perfectionists will find the flaw in anything. This often includes self-denigration and self-doubt. If I were to ask you to quickly tell me ten things that you really do well, what would you list? The true perfectionist would struggle to come up with five things because, as each thought occurred, the perfectionist's inner dialogue would say, "Well, I'm good at it, but not really good" or "I am good at it, but someone is better." Either way, there is no self-appreciation or acceptance here, just self-criticism.

If I ask a five-year-old child the same question, most would immediately rattle off a list of things they can do well. Most young children have not learned perfectionism by this age.

Here is one of the best tools to begin to let go of perfectionism: before going to bed, think of three things that you did well today, and be thankful for them. While this sounds ridiculously simple, it is extremely powerful. Try it for a week. You will see the change.

The Illusion of Central Positioning

A good deal of stress can come from the feeling that someone is trying to get you or that another's behavior is somehow related to you. This occurs very commonly in miscommunication scenarios. When an interaction is unclear with someone, you may jump to the conclusion that that person is mad at you or doesn't like you, or that you did something wrong. An example of this is when someone walks by, whom you acknowledge, but who doesn't acknowledge you. In this situation the person probably didn't hear you, was lost in thought about something, or was physically unwell. We often jump to, "What did I do wrong?" essentially making it about us. If you think about the other possibilities triggering the person's lack of response, the chance that you inadvertently did something wrong is the least likely possibility. This would be the self-doubtful, self-critical version of trying to read someone's mind. What you are doing is projecting your own self-involvement onto another. This has been called the *illusion of central positioning;* it's all about you.

The illusion of centricity gets us into interpersonal trouble at home too. Have you ever told your children to pick up their socks and yet they continually leave the socks lying about? On still seeing the socks on the floor, most of us might instantly get the feeling that our children don't respect us or even that they are doing it intentionally to annoy us. This, too, is the illusion of central positioning, believing that it is about you. Kids leave socks on the floor, husbands don't fold towels, and spouses leave lights on, not intentionally to get to you, but because they don't think about these things. Taking it personally makes it much more aggravating for you, and more catecholamines are spilled in the process.

While I am writing this chapter, I am sitting in my living room while my fifteen-year old son is downstairs at his computer. He is on vacation this week. Last night I asked him to clean his room and give his dog a bath. He picked up a few things but the dog has yet to be washed. These are simple tasks: clean room, clean dog. He is on vacation with no responsibility. The reason he is not responding quickly to my demands is that he has to catch up on all the video-game playing he missed out on last semester, especially the one he got for Christmas. This is at the top of his priority list. Clean room and clean dog are low on his list. If I believed that this was about me, I would be really aggravated. Fortunately I know that it is not. So my healthy response is to go down there every so often and say, "Clean room, clean dog," in almost a lighthearted way. This way he is more likely to respond, and when he does, I will say, "Good job," not "Why didn't you do it last night?" This acknowledges his paying attention to my needs, which are not on his list, and may positively reinforce other changes in the future. At some point, if the task is not done, I may have to restrict him in some way, but as long as I stay clear that his lack of motivation is unrelated to me, then I can stay calm. My guess is, by tonight the room will be clean enough.*

The illusion of central positioning is one of the worst enemies of the type-A person. Why are they doing this to me? Why do some people in the grocery express lane have twelve, instead of ten, items? Don't they know I am busy? Don't they know that I am a doctor and have important things to do? This mentality spills a huge amount of catecholamines and cortisol, and can lead you to a heart attack, while the people with more than ten items go merrily on their way. Is it worth it to get upset about such situations?

Worrying and Negative Conclusions

We tend to burn up energy worrying about things before they happen, whether it's about a phone call we have to make, about our children being late, or about what our colleagues think of us. A good example is a friend of mine, who was named in a lawsuit while on staff at a major university. He was one of many physicians on the patient's record during her admission, and all were named. His first worry was, "Did I do something wrong?" and even after he realized that he didn't do harm, he continued to perseverate on this concern. His next worry emerged when he found out that he had to be interviewed by the oversight committee to give his side of the case. He spent two weeks, several restless nights, and many catecholamines worrying about this meeting. If you asked him what was likely the intention for the meeting, he would probably have said, "They just need to get my story," but he could not shut off the "worry" button. He later revealed that the worry was not about the case, but what his colleagues would think of his being named in a lawsuit. These days, this is not rational though understandable. On the day of the meeting, he walked into the boardroom and everyone was light and pleasant. They apologized for taking up his time, asked him a few questions, and then went out to lunch. He had wasted two weeks of catecholamines and lost a whole lot of sleep for nothing!

If worry is a tendency of yours, I encourage you to keep a simple "worry record," in any notepad. When you find yourself worrying about something, write down on the left margin the event that has you worried, in the center write your belief about what will happen, and eventually, in the right column write down what actually happened after the event is over. See the example below:

Event that I am worried about	My belief	The actual outcome

This also serves as a restructuring tool. It will help you to shift from your old congested ways of thinking into more flexible ways of thinking. Do this exercise for two weeks and you will see how frequently your worrying mind is wrong.

Generalizing

Generalizing is making a statement as if it were always true, 100 percent of the time. In generalizing, the words *always* and *never* appear frequently. Any of you with a spouse who uses always or never accusations knows how bad this feels and how it usually inflames a situation. These accusations put your loved one in a position of being wrong 100 percent of the time. Is this true? How often do you do this to those you love?

Next time you use always or never with your spouse or loved one, ask yourself how often the event really happens. If someone you know is "always" late, is it 60 percent of the time, 80 percent of the time? Always and never are literally exaggerations. It's no wonder that the other person becomes defensive.

My wife Kathy used to "always" run late. The reality was that I was compulsively on time and she was a multitasker. When we were getting ready to go someplace, I would start to become impatient twenty minutes before time to leave, as I watched her multitask without focusing on getting ready. Internally I fussed that she was always late and was mad at her even before she was actually late. My hovering and impatience would make her anxious, and by the time we actually left (usually five to ten minutes later than I wanted), I was livid and so was she.

The internal dynamic here was that I felt that she didn't respect me (illusion of centricity), while she thought that if she didn't get the e-mail out, the bill wouldn't be paid. If I then said (or yelled), "You're always late!" she would get defensive, and the next hour would be a miserable one.

What's the fix here? The first task is to acknowledge that my compulsion to be early is my issue and a part of my type-A structure. The second is to acknowledge that her multitasking and lateness are her way of being, which I am very unlikely to change. The third task is to find a way to be on time when I truly need to be on time, such as when giving a lecture. And the fourth task is to answer the question, "Can I love her anyhow?" For me the answer has always been yes.

Some of you may read this and think that I am the perfect guy. Give it up! I am still type A, although in recovery, and still have many relapses. Just ask my wife.

Walls

Some mistakes in relationships are subtle. One that I caution you against is using the words good, fine, or okay to answer the question, "How are you?" While on a supermarket or tollbooth line, such responses are appropriate, but with someone you care about, they are a way of distancing yourself. Try to be more descriptive with your answer, such as, "I am really energetic today" or "I am tired." This let's people know how you really are. If you are not well and don't want to talk about it, just say something like, "It's not a good day, but I don't feel like talking." This will just lead to sympathy, which is connecting.

Your Reality

Very often we become locked into thinking that our thoughts are the only possible reality.

While our beliefs may be grounded in experience or our preferences, it is important to understand that many of them may not be true for others.

This became very clear to me when I began to travel to other countries. I grew up believing that people should line up for things and wait their turn. I would also get agitated when people didn't follow this (my) rule. In traveling to Asia for the first time, I realized that lining up is a very European mind-set. In fact, even though people in Asia often jump in front of each other, there is very little malice or anger in the process. So whose perspective is a healthy one, the American who gets road rage on being cut off by another driver, or the Asian who laughs about it?

Our thoughts come from our experiences and the experiences of those around us, such as our parents, teachers, religious leaders, and society. Thoughts vary by region, race, cultural background, and even gender. Getting locked into your belief system is a major stress inducer. I encourage you to ask yourself the simple question, "Is it possible that I am wrong or that others may feel differently than I do?"

"Shoulds" are another part of our reality and essentially, they are judgments. "People should or shouldn't do X, Y, or Z"; or "I should be a better person," "I should be more attentive," "I should lose weight," or "I shouldn't make any mistakes." These statements are self-abusive and lead to guilt and frustration. Who makes up these rules? They may be societal in nature or may have come from your family or your religion. It doesn't matter what the source is, some "shoulds" do more harm than good. Think of the average person looking at a fitness magazine cover and concluding that he or she should look like the cover model. Most people, on looking in the mirror, do just that. The result is self-dissatisfaction and unhappiness. The resulting actions are often fad diets, cosmetic surgery, and depression. Who made up the rules about how people should look? Marketing executives who want you to buy their products. This is the fallacy of the "should."

I encourage you to question each "should" as it arises. You may wish to keep some, and others you may want to let go of. A friend once said to me that there would be no wars if there were no judgments — a powerful thought indeed!

Reclaim Your Thoughts — The ABCD method
(A Restructuring Tool — Thirty Minutes)

The ABCD method of shifting perspectives was created by Albert Ellis.[2] It serves as a simple, yet reasonable, way to evaluate your current perspective and look for a new one. This can be used to correct any mistaken thinking. In the following box, write down an event (activating event) that caused you stress. It can be anything that annoys you. Next, write down your initial beliefs (belief square) about that event. The belief is your usual thought or judgment about that event. Then write down the emotional consequences of those beliefs (how this event makes you feel). This is where we usually end up after an annoying event, in an emotional state. This never moves us to a solution. Now, pause, take a deep breath, and think of any other possible perspectives (disputes) to those beliefs and consequences. How might you perceive this differently? What might have been going on for the other person? Once you come up with possible disputes, it's easier to find solutions. Use this tool to gain a new perspective when you have a situation that repeatedly annoys. Let's take a work-related event as an example:

Event
There are no large exam gloves in the exam room.

Belief
Why don't they restock the large gloves? They know I have large hands (centricity). These people are worthless (judgment) or they don't care.

Consequences
Anger

Now, let's look at the disputes. What else might be going on here? Let's make an expansive list:

- We don't order enough gloves.
- The storage area is too far away to be accessible.
- They don't know in advance which doctor will be using which room each day.
- We don't have enough storage space in the exam rooms.
- We need to restock the rooms more frequently.
- They hate me and are out to get me.

As you can see, by listing all the possibilities, you can start to find solutions to problems instead of just getting stuck in an emotional consequence such as wailing around mad all day. Give this a try with the box below and repeat this exercise using multiple issues that bug you.

> *God, grant me the serenity to accept the things I cannot change, the courage to change the things I can, and the wisdom to know the difference.*

> — The Serenity Prayer
> Attributed to theologian Reinhold Niebuhr, circa 1934

ABCD method box

Activating Event (what happened)	Consequences (What emotions or behaviors developed) Angry, hopeless, depressed
Beliefs (Your immediate thoughts and assumptions) "I should have known better" "I hate myself" "It's their fault, not mine"	Disputes (New thoughts) "I guess it really wasn't that bad" "She probably didn't mean what I thought shemeant"

CHAPTER 1 Emotional Shifting and Emotional Intelligence

In this chapter, I will show you how you can use your own emotions to manage stress, improve performance, and gain flexibility. These are the best crisis management power tools that I have ever practiced. Take an hour to read this chapter and practice the exercises. Then spend a week practicing these tools to gauge their full impact. These tools become stronger and easier to use with practice.

The first tool you will learn is emotional shifting, the art of substituting one emotional response for another, hopefully more desirable, response. The application of this is fairly simple. The first step is to recognize something that disturbs you, so awareness is a key element. Once you recognize the disturbance, you can learn to shift your emotional response to the situation or person.

Emotional shifting can also be used to help you reenergize or refocus when you feel yourself getting caught up in overemotionality. This will help you to block your usual mistakes in thinking, especially generalizing and maximizing negative circumstances, as discussed previously. I will also show you how emotional shifting enhances cortical function and emotional intelligence.

Emotional shifting techniques differ from other commonly used stress management approaches in several key respects. Unlike meditation and relaxation techniques, which focus on calming or quieting the mind and body, emotional shifting involves actively engaging or creating a positive emotional state, which favorably affects both physiological and mental processes. Emotional shifting techniques are distinct from visualization methods in that their emphasis is upon genuinely reexperiencing a positive feeling state, rather than simply calling up a pleasant mental memory or image. Recalling the feeling state helps shift the emotion out of the cognitive level and appears to have a greater physiological impact than visualization. To begin this process, we must identify positive emotions to engage.

I believe that you will understand this better through experience. Make a list or just think of all the things in your life that are disturbing you at the moment. Close your eyes as you think of these things, and see what it feels like. Pay attention to where you feel this in your body.

Some of you might get tightness in the chest; increased heart rate; tightness in the head, neck, or shoulders; or even a queasy feeling in the gut. This is all driven by an elevation in catecholamines, almost instantaneously with your thoughts. It is important to realize that the thought is the driver of the physiologic response; the event does not even have to occur to create an internal physiologic response. This is true for all stress responses; they are generalized and can be triggered as easily by a thought as by an action. When we discuss how perspective, personality issues, judgments, and "shoulds" cause stress, this is exactly the mechanism. Thought precedes and changes physiology.

Now let's do an emotional shift. The first step would be to identify what is going well for you in your life today. It may be useful to write a list of things that are going well. I would ask that you close your eyes and think of the positive events, people, and attributes of your life. See how this feels in your body and try to identify where you feel it.

Positive thoughts trigger a different physiologic cascade. Firstly, catecholamines and cortisol decrease, making the body feel lighter. Then dopamine is released, giving you the warm and fuzzy feeling. There are other neurochemicals released as well. I will discuss more of this later in the chapter. Remember, the thought drives the physiologic response.

Identifying Positive Emotions

Let's now identify some additional emotions that might serve you well here. Consider each of the following and see how you feel:

- Think of a place that is peaceful. Close your eyes and imagine yourself there. Feel and smell the air. How do you feel physically and emotionally when you are in this place? Try to reexperience those feelings with your eyes closed for a minute.
- Think of someone you truly love and, with your eyes closed, picture that person standing before you. Pay attention to your loved one's eyes and focus your attention on how you feel in your body. Remember the feeling of love, and hold that feeling for one minute.
- Now think of an activity that you find fun and exciting, and try to re-experience the sense of excitement for one minute.

These are the emotions you can use in making emotional shifts. Loving seems to work best for me in almost any circumstance, unless I am mad at the person I love. The fun and exciting one works when I am in a low-energy state or fatigued, and the peaceful one works when I am agitated. I'd suggest that you try each feeling state over and over to see what effect they have on you.

Internal Stress and Perception

Let's now apply some of the positive emotions that we identified through the previous exercises to stress-inducing situations. I want to suggest the example of seeing someone you dislike walk down a hallway toward you. Close your eyes and imagine the scenario. How does it feel? Are you tense, angry, upset, or cringing? This is a catecholamine response brought about by a thought. It is impressive how your mind can control your body. The person you chose is probably someone you've known for a while. For discussion, let's say that this guy or women is a real jerk whom we will call *Dr. X.* Every time you see him or her, Dr. X reminds you about something you didn't do, an article you didn't read, or how great Dr. X is. After seeing Dr. X regularly for many years, your midbrain has been trained to respond to this person as a stressor (a Pavlovian training response). You also start to see Dr. X as worse than he or she probably is. Dr. X has become "always" bad. Just thinking about Dr. X triggers the response, so Dr. X wins! This then affects your physiology with high catecholamines and cortisol.

Why do we amplify others' bad behaviors in our minds and thus the response? I believe that this is a self-protective mechanism. We are preparing ourselves for the worst possible outcome that can happen, but in doing so, we spill the greatest amount of catecholamine possible. Essentially, we are letting others take control of our physiology. It's time to take it back!

Experiential Activity
Get into a comfortable position, close your eyes, and start thinking about the annoying person. Feel the tension (catecholamines) increase. Now, because this is your mind and you are in control (not the other person), start thinking about one of the positive emotions that you previously identified (peaceful, loving, or fun). Breathe very deeply and slowly while thinking of the positive emotion. Hold this state of positive emotion and deep breathing for at least one minute. Pay attention to how you feel mentally and emotionally. Is the discomfort lighter?

We are using your breathing to abort the catecholamine response to your thought and then move the thought away from the agitating person. This is a technique called *Quick Coherence,* by HeartMath. I will discuss the physiologic response in greater detail later in the chapter. For now, think "shift" your breathing and "activate" a positive emotion.

If you practice this shifting process when around the annoying person, you will retrain your meso-limbic response. This is a Pavlovian retraining technique and is extraordinarily effective. Keep in mind that Dr. X will still be Dr. X, but you won't have elevated catecholamines any more. The more you practice this, the less effect Dr. X will have on your physiology.

Another way to think about this Quick Coherence technique is that it allows you to respond in a better way to external stresses. This has proven highly effective for me personally. An example occurred during a work trip to Florida. I traveled from the West Coast to Boca Raton to do a keynote presentation. I arrived at my hotel at 11:00 PM, only to find that they had me scheduled to arrive the next day. At that moment I took a deep breath (shift) and moved (activate) my thoughts to snuggling with my wife. The hotel clerk then checked for room availability, but there were no rooms left (shift and activate). I then asked if I could connect with the meeting organizer. She was not in her room (shift and activate), so I left a message for her. I then asked if there were other hotels nearby. The clerk began to call, and after three tries (shift and activate), there were no rooms. She then handed the bellman and me a list, and we all began calling (shift and activate). After a few attempts, the bellman reminded us that it was spring break (shift and activate). As we continued to call, I scanned the lobby and noticed a far corner at the side of the building with a couch and large plants. I knew that, if worse came to worst, I could crash there (we doctors can sleep anywhere), and no one would notice.

After the three of us had exhausted our lists, I told the staff that I would just go have a seat and wait until I heard back from the meeting planner. So I went to my couch, shifted and activated, and began to read the book I had with me. All the time, I kept the thought in my mind that no matter what happened, the next night I would be home in bed with my wife. This activated emotion kept me calm, and the deep breathing kept my catecholamines from going up.

Eventually, the very apologetic meeting planner called me, and I firmly (but not angrily) asked her to help me find a place to stay. She ended up calling the company president, who graciously offered me half of his two-room suite.

If this had happened to me ten years earlier, before I knew the Heartmath technique, I would have lost my temper, agitated those around me, and maybe never been asked to speak again there. The fact that I stayed calm impressed everyone, including the meeting planner and president, and we have had a nice working relationship ever since. All of this was due to shifting and activating.

HeartMath uses a very simple equation: Event + Response = Outcome. The only part of the equation under your control is the response. The Quick Coherence technique helps you respond in an emotionally intelligent way.

This technique can be expanded into what Heartmath refers to as the *Freeze-Frame* technique. Freeze-framing is a problem-solving technique akin to the ABCD technique in the preceding chapter. The difference here is that you use emotions to shift away from your current perspective into a new perspective or solution.

The following instructions are adapted from and courtesy of HeartMath LLC. For more information, publications, and software contact: HeartMath, 14700 W. Park Avenue, Boulder Creek, California 95006, 800-450-9511 or www.heartmath.com.

Freeze-Frame Instructions:

1. Take time out so that you can temporarily disengage from you thoughts and feelings. especially the stressful ones.
2. Shift your focus to the area around your heart. Now feel your breath coming in through your heart and out through your solar plexus. Practice breathing this way a few times to ease into the technique.

3. Make a sincere effort to activate a positive feeling. This can be a genuine feeling of appreciation or care for a person, a place, or anything in your life.

4. Ask yourself what would be a more efficient, effective attitude or action that would balance and de-stress your system.

5. Quietly sense any change in perception or feeling and sustain it as long as you can. Heart perceptions are often subtle. They gently suggest effective solutions that would be best for you and all concerned.

When using the above technique, I suggest that you write down the situation that causes you stress. Then write your usual thoughts about the situation and the emotions that arise. Do the technique for as long as it takes to arrive at a new way of responding to the situation. This may come immediately or may take many sessions. I encourage you to practice this technique, focusing on those people or situations in your life that push your buttons. Do this at least three times today to get the feel for it.

For a more detailed look into this area and additional techniques, I recommend *The HeartMath Solution* by Doc Childre and Howard Martin.[1]

Emotional Shifting Applications

Emotional shifting has been applied in work (including hospitals and clinics), school, and clinical environments. These techniques have been shown to reduce stress, depression, and negative emotions, while enhancing positive emotions, communication, and job satisfaction.[2, 3, 4, 5] Additionally, practice of the techniques has been shown to have significant physiological benefits, including enhancing autonomic nervous system balance as measured by HRV,[6, 7] reducing cortisol levels and increasing DHEA,[4] boosting immunity,[5, 8] reducing blood pressure in hypertensive individuals,[3] and improving exercise capacity in people with congestive heart failure.[9] Emotional shifting techniques have also been applied to decrease Hgb A1c in a diabetic population.[10] This is likely due to decreases in catecholamines and cortisol, both of which enhance gluconeogenesis and glycogenolysis.

Emotional Shifting and Cortical Function When shifting from an angry, hostile, or depressive thought to a mood state of appreciation that is in tune with your values, there is an interesting neurophysiological shift that occurs. The first effect is a decreased release of catecholamines. This triggers an alteration of output from the vagus nerve to the body. This shift in vagal tone triggers a shift in HRV, which sends feedback information to the cortex, via the midbrain, to help facilitate cortical function. In simple terms, when you relax and get happy, you get smarter. This is the physiology behind the concept of emotional intelligence. Below is a detailed description of this physiology and some of the research. Much of this work has been done at the Institute of HeartMath (www.heartmath.org).

In your life, you have known this experience functionally. Have you ever awoken with an answer to a problem that had bothered you? Was it a solution that now seemed obvious? Has this ever happened to you after a good workout? Exercise, sleep, meditation, and other relaxation techniques all lead to decreased catecholamines and increased cortical function. Therefore, in a low-catecholamine state, you have better cortical access, meaning that you will find answers to problems more readily.

How can you do this while in a stressful situation? If you practice emotional shifting on a routine basis, you can learn to do it while on your feet. Right now, take a few deep breaths and think of someone you love. Try to feel the sensation of love in your body. How does that feel? Where do you feel it? Practice this at least once an hour for the next day. You'll see that a shift happens for you.

Heart Rate Variability Heart Rate Variability (HRV) is the beat-to-beat change in heart rate. As sympathetic tone increases, the heartbeats (R to R interval on the EKG) get closer together. As parasympathetic tone increases, they widen out. The ebb and flow of autonomic tone create patterns of heart rate slowing and accelerating. Thus HRV is an indicator of autonomic function.

There are two basic patterns of HRV (see graphic, courtesy of the Institute of HeartMath). The low pattern represents high sympathetic tone. When sympathetic tone is chronically elevated, as seen in depression, anger, anxiety, and hostility (emotions not uncommon in medicine), parasympathetic tone also increases the attempt to achieve homeostasis. Without this, you would have unopposed sympathetic stimulation and a heart rate of over 220 beats per minute. In a simple, but reasonable, analogy, it is like running your car with your foot on the gas and brake at the same time. Low HRV is called that because the peak-to-nadir difference in the waveform is small or low. High HRV patterning represents a balanced, cohesive ebb and flow of sympathetic and parasympathetic tone. This occurs when both tonalities are at modest to low output.

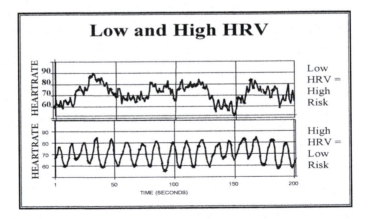

HRV is another likely link between adverse cardiac events and emotional states. Low HRV is associated with high sympathetic tone. High sympathetic tone is associated with increased arrhythmias, vasoreactivity, hypercoagulabilty, and thrombosis.[11] Low HRV patterning is also associated with higher risk of sudden death and MI in patients with CAD.[12-15]

Low HRV is also found in individuals with CAD, who are emotionally depressed when compared with those who are not depressed. In the Carney et al. study of individuals post-MI, those who were depressed (major and minor) had low HRV compared to those who were not depressed. HRV was equally low in those who had major depression, minor depression, or dysthymia, when compared to those without depressive symptoms.[15]

The Institute of HeartMath has demonstrated that various emotions affect HRV patterning.[6] In one study, power spectral density (PSD) analysis of HRV was used to compare autonomic activation and sympathovagal balance in subjects during a five-minute baseline period, in contrast to a five-minute period of self-induced anger and a five-minute period of appreciation induced by the Freeze-Frame technique (an emotional shifting technique previously mentioned). It was found that both anger and appreciation caused an increase in autonomic activation, as demonstrated by an increase in power in all frequencies of the HRV power spectrum and in mean heart rate standard deviation. The two emotional states produced different effects on sympathovagal balance. Anger produced a sympathetically dominated power spectrum; appreciation produced a power spectral shift toward increased parasympathetic activity.[7] These shifts were correlated with shifts in HRV patterning to one that is healthier and not predictive of cardiac adverse events. Therefore shifting to and maintaining a sincere positive emotion may shift your physiology toward overall better health. This may explain why people with an optimistic outlook on life have significantly lower mortality than those who are generally pessimistic.[16]

HeartMath Emotional Stress Treatment Projects The following two studies are examples of the multiple workplace interventions delivered by HeartMath since 1991.

In a study of employees of a state agency in California, a HeartMath teaching intervention showed dramatic results in emotional outcomes. The HeartMath training was delivered over the course of six weeks to 54 employees. Participants spent time learning and applying the HeartMath emotional shifting tools and techniques to the issues, challenges, and opportunities inherent in fundamental organizational change. A psychological survey measuring dimensions of stress, emotions, and organizational effectiveness was administered during pre- and post-training. Results were compared with a comparison group of 64 employees who were awaiting training.

After the completion of the training, seven weeks from the initial assessment, the HeartMath group demonstrated significant reductions in measures of stress and negative emotion, and significant increases in measures of positive emotion and organizational effectiveness in relation to the comparison group. Key findings after the training indicated significant decreases in anger (20 percent), distress (21 percent), depression (26 percent), sadness (22 percent), and fatigue (24 percent); and significant increases in peacefulness (23 percent) and vitality

(10 percent). There was also a reduction in stress symptoms, including anxiety (21 percent), sleeplessness (24 percent), and rapid heartbeats (19 percent). Organizational quality assessment revealed significant gains in goal clarity (9 percent) and productivity (4 percent). These changes were noteworthy in light of the major organizational and emotional challenges faced by the participants, and the relatively short time in which the improvements took place. Results suggest that by facilitating increased self-management of participants' mental and emotional turmoil, the HeartMath interventions enhanced employees' capacity to defuse personal and organizational stress.

A study of police officers trained in the HeartMath techniques demonstrated decreased stress, negative emotions, and fatigue; increased calmness and clarity under the acute stress of simulated police calls; and more rapid recalibration following these high-stress scenarios, as compared to an untrained control group.[10] In contrast, officers in the control group showed minimal positive changes and some indications of the worsening of symptoms over the same period. Notably feelings of depression rose 17 percent among the untrained officers, while the HeartMath-trained group demonstrated a 13 percent drop in depression during the same period. Similarly, fatigue declined among the HeartMath group by 18 percent and distress by 20 percent, whereas the control group demonstrated only a 1 percent reduction in both these parameters. Enhanced work performance in the trained group was also noted, as well as improvements in strained family relationships and communication difficulties at work, two principal and well-recognized sources of stress in the policing profession. What if you and your staff could decrease your stress and increase your performance at the same time? All it takes is practice in the techniques that you are learning in this program.

Gaining emotional intelligence - When you are in a high-catecholamine, high-cortisol, low-HRV state, your cortex is inhibited. The opposite is true when you are in a low-catecholamine, high-HRV state. You can enhance your cortical function and emotional intelligence with emotional shifting, meditation, prayer, and deep breathing.

HRV affects your emotions and cortical function, but you can control HRV. The HRV shift is greatest when you shift from a state of frustration, anxiety, hostility, or depression to an emotional state of appreciation, caring, or loving. Voluntary practices such as prayer and mantras positively affect HRV. The greatest effect on HRV is seen when cyclic respiration is combined with positive emotions. This will affect your cortical function and perception. Your perception and cortical function are within your control.

CHAPTER 12 **Connection**

Interpersonal connection is one of the strongest maintenance tools you can have. It should be attended to daily! Most of us have a sense of the importance of connecting with other people in our lives. Many of us would consider our lives empty, perhaps not even worth living, if it weren't for the people we love. There are many levels in which deep personal connection affects our emotional and physical well-being. This chapter reviews literature on health observations, outcomes, and physiology as it relates to interpersonal connection. In the next chapter you will also learn communication techniques based on the information presented. For additional reading in this area, I refer you to the book, *Love and Survival*, by Dr. Dean Ornish.

Connection with Parents

Let's first look at the literature on interpersonal connection in the family and its impact on health. The Harvard Mastery of Stress Study was a thirty-five-year longitudinal look at medical students and their life habits, skills, and relationships. The study evaluated these issues and their effect on the students' health into midlife. An intriguing outcome was the correlation of the students' relationships with their parents and the students' midlife health. The worse the relationship was, the more likely the student was to have significant chronic health issues.

Relationships with parents were described as being very close, warm and friendly, tolerant, or strained and cold. Thirty-five years later, follow-up studies showed that if the relationship with the mother was tolerant or strained, 91 percent of the participants had a significant health issue. By comparison, if the relationship with the mother was close and warm, half the number had a significant health issue. The relationship with the father was slightly less predictive of subsequent health concerns, with 82 percent having a significant health issue if the relationship was tolerant or strained, and 50 percent having a significant health issue if the relationship was warm and close. If the relationship with both parents was strained, there was a 100 percent incidence of significant health risk, compared to a 47 percent risk if the relationship with both parents was warm and close.[1]

There are many variables that affect health outcomes later in life, and the researchers were aware of these variables. Some of the variables are related to various aspects of the individuals' upbringing. The authors stated the following reasons why these outcomes were so striking:

1. Nutrition, stress, and loving energy — before and after birth — will contribute to the health of the individual.
2. Healthy and unhealthy lifestyle behaviors develop in childhood.
3. Coping styles such as anxiety, anger, optimism, and self-esteem develop in childhood.
4. Choices of stable relationships in adulthood are often mirrors of parental relationship.

5. Healthy relationship with a parent usually means the presence of a supportive parent in adulthood.

6. Spiritual values and practices are developed in childhood.

A similar fifty-year study at Johns Hopkins University, studying rates of suicide, mental illness, malignant tumor, hypertension, and coronary artery disease (CAD), showed almost the same correlations with disease. If the relationship with the parent was not healthy, there was nearly a doubling in the rates of illness. These findings were independent of smoking, alcohol use, or radiation exposures. The correlation was strongest in the development of cancer.[2]

These two studies strongly suggest a relationship between the connection of parent with the child and the subsequent health of that child. There have been other such studies, but these two are the most complete and most representative. It is also important that the authors of these studies accounted for other disease risks and that the results were independent of these risks.

While there is no research-based evidence that improving your relationships can reverse these trends, it is fair to say that your attitudes and sense of acceptance and forgiveness can be shifted. Based on the studies cited below, it is also reasonable to assume that even with difficult early relationships, other healthy relationships in marriage and friendship will enhance your health.

In addition, if you look for the parts of your early relationships that were pleasant and focus on those parts, negative feelings toward your parents can shift into forgiveness. What do you appreciate the most about how you were raised? How has this affected your life today? This is good content for a meditation of appreciation.

Connection in Marriage
Let's look at how marital relationships affect health. Medalie and Goldbourt did a study of ten-thousand men over a five-year period. The men chosen had three or more risk factors for CAD (such as being over forty-five years old, or having elevated cholesterol, HTN, diabetes, or EKG abnormalities), and were estimated to be twenty times more likely to develop angina than men without those risks. The researchers were looking for the ability of relationship qualities to predict or correlate with the development of anginal symptoms. Men within the high-risk group who answered yes to the question, "Does your wife show you her love?" had half the development of angina compared to those who responded no. It is interesting to note that the predictive question revolved around the demonstration of love, not just knowing that you are loved. It is possible that men need to hear the words, whereas women more readily can trust their inner knowing.[3]

Another project looked at relationship, or lack of relationship, as a predictor of mortality in patients with CAD. This study looked at men and women (1,400 total) who underwent cardiac catheterization and were found to have CAD.

These patients were given various questionnaires on relationships in their lives and were then followed for five years for clinical outcomes. Two key questions, predictive of survival, were (1) "Are you married?" and (2) "Do you have someone in whom you can confide?" After five years, roughly 15 percent of patients who were married or had a confidant were dead, while 50 percent of those who were unmarried and had no confidant were dead.[4]

These two studies are good examples of the power of marital relationships. Other studies have shown the following:

1. Men who are shown love by their wives have fewer gastric ulcers.
2. Married men and women live longer.
3. People who are in happy marriages live longer than people who are not.
4. Couples who argue more have lower immune function and more frequent respiratory infections.
5. People with CAD, who live alone, have twice the rate of MI as people who live with someone else.

All of these studies point to one fact: happy marriage and companionship are good for your health, independent of other risk factors.

Social Isolation versus Social Embeddedness

The presence of multiple healthy relationships is called social embeddedness. Multiple studies have shown that the lack of social embeddedness, or social isolation, enhances risk of disease. It is important to realize that social isolates can be with many people throughout the day, at work and at home, but have no real sense of connection with others. This is unusual in physicians because we are good connectors. However, I do see this in physicians who have a high degree of narcissism.

In a study looking at social isolation and heart disease, 149 men and women who were to undergo cardiac catheterization were questioned about the degree to which they felt loved and supported. These were individuals suspected of having coronary disease because of their symptoms. The number and size of blockages found on subsequent angiograms correlated positively with the degree of love and support. This was independent of other predictive variables such as smoking.[5]

Social embeddedness within the community also impacts your health. A fifty-year observational study of the towns of Roseto, Bangor, and Nazareth, Pennsylvania, demonstrated this nicely. In the 1930s and 1940s, it was noted that the town of Roseto, Pennsylvania, had a significantly lower rate of acute MIs than neighboring communities; yet diabetes, obesity, and high-fat diet all seemed to be equally present in the three towns. During the follow-up, the rate of MI and overall mortality had a substantial increase in Roseto, but not the other towns. This increase occurred in the early and late 1970s. When health behaviors such as smoking, weight, diet, and diabetes were analyzed, there were still no significant differences in the three communities over the study period that could account for these changes. What had changed in this period was the social structure of Roseto. Roseto, which had been populated by descendents from Roseto in southern Italy in the late 1800s, had closer family ties, evidenced by a much greater number of three-generation households and churchgoers. As these ties began to disintegrate in the late 1960s, with the deaths of the original immigrants and the younger generations moving on, the rates of MI and mortality began to rise. It is important to note that this effect was independent of usual cardiac risk factors such as smoking, obesity, and diabetes.

This is the longest and clearest of the multiple studies of communities showing a distinct relationship among community activity, social structure, and the rates of disease. It also points toward the role of religious practice and its effect on disease prevalence.[6]

In a related study and subsequent book, Berkman and Breslow surveyed and followed 6,900 men and women in Alameda County, California. The key determinant of health outcomes were contact with friends and relatives, church membership, membership in clubs or groups, and marriage. Those without close ties or frequent social contact had an overall death rate 3.1 times higher than those who did have such contacts. Both men and women in the low-connection category had higher cancer death rates. An analysis was done on breast cancer patients that found that those with low connection had twice the death rate, regardless of race.[7]

These and other studies indicated that social isolation and a perceived lack of social connection are significant risk factors for CAD, cancer, and other mortality. It is important to note that social isolation reported in these studies was self-reported, and this risk may therefore be related to the individual's perception of isolation. The issue of perception versus the effect of actual contact has not been tested in these studies. However, as I will outline below, perception is likely to be a contributor to, and possibly a more significant health modifier, than the actual interpersonal connection.

Social Connection as Intervention
Because of the observation and earlier suspicion of the effect of social connection on disease risk, researchers have studied the effectiveness of social connection as an intervention, or as part of an intervention, to treat disease states.

David Spiegel at Stanford University conducted one of the first and most intriguing studies in this area. The patient and control groups were comprised of women with metastatic breast cancer. A once-weekly, ninety-minute group support session was used as an intervention for one year. No other changes were made in the therapy delivered by their primary physicians or oncologists. Follow-up occurred over five years.

The initial hypothesis was that group support would help these women adjust to their disease, as well as help with anxiety, depression, and other psychosocial issues. The outcomes supported this hypothesis. For the authors of the study, a more dramatic and surprising outcome was that the group-support patients lived twice as long as the control group, eighteen versus nine months on average.[8]

In a similar study, patients, post-local resection of malignant melanoma, were placed in a six-week support group. They were then followed for five to six years. No other intervention was used. At the five-year mark, the control group had experienced thirteen recurrences and ten deaths, while the study group had had seven recurrences and three deaths.

These results achieved statistical significance. It is important to note that if statistical significance is achieved in a small group study, the power of the intervention is much greater as long as there are no outliers. Conversely, if you need thousands of people over many more years to achieve a significant difference, it indicates that the treatment effect is weak.[9]

It is important to note that the health effects of connection are not necessarily related to accentuating the positive. The above groups were not intended to be "feel good" groups. These groups were to aid the patient in being open and vulnerable with significant health and relationship issues. In fact, the greatest benefits appear to occur when an individual has a safe place to manage negative emotions and work through them with a group.[10]

The most valuable gift you can give to another person is your attention.

— Art Brownstein, MD

The Healing Physiology of Connection

In some way, being socially integrated reduces all-cause age-adjusted mortality by a factor of twofold, about as much as having low versus high serum-cholesterol levels or being a nonsmoker.[11] How can the lack of interpersonal connection be an equivalent for heart disease to the same extent as elevated cholesterol? What do we know about the underlying mechanisms for the effects measured in the preceding studies?

Intentional connection (group support), interpersonal connection (marriage, friendship, and pets), and community connection (such as participation in church or social groups) have all been shown to decrease life stress. Life stress is internally mediated through the release of catecholamines, cortisol (if chronic), and probably other neurohormonal mechanisms. Social isolation is associated with elevated catecholamines and cortisol.[12] This is very likely a contributing mechanism.

Depression is also linked with multiple diseases such as cancer, sudden death, and CAD. In multiple studies, Nancy Frazier-Smith demonstrated that social support ameliorates this effect in heart patients. Social support does not necessarily eliminate the depression, but it does eliminate the adverse health outcomes of the depression as well as the catecholamine and cortisol elevations usually found in depressed people.[13]

Immunologic Mechanisms

If social connection helps to improve cancer outcomes, it seems likely that some of the benefits of social connection also may come through immunologic mechanisms. To understand this relationship, one must consider the realm of psychoneuroimmunology (PNI). In the book, *Psychoneuroimmunology*,[14] the editors describe the basic evidence to support the connection of the mind, the nervous system, and the immune system. They include the following:

- Nerve endings are found in the tissues of the immune system (bone marrow, thymus, spleen, and lymph nodes).
- Changes in hormonal and neurotransmitter levels alter immune responsiveness and vice versa.
- Immunization alters hormonal output.
- Cortisol suppresses immune function (cortisol is elevated with social isolation).
- Changes in the central nervous system cause alteration in immune function and vice versa.
- Hypothalamic damage suppresses allergic response.
- Immune activation increases hypothalamic activity.
- Lymphocytes are chemically responsive to hormones and neurotransmitters via surface receptors.
- Interleukens and interferons, produced by activated lymphocytes, are detected in the CNS. CNS cells have receptors for these substances.
- Psychosocial factors have been shown to affect the susceptibility to, or the progression of, autoimmune diseases, infection, and cancer.
- Immunologic reactivity is altered by stress.
- Immunologic reactivity can be classically trained through a placebo effect.</>

There have been a number of clinical observations to support this as well. Caregivers of dementia patients have decreased immune responsiveness and increased upper-respiratory infections. Caregivers with good social support outside of the home have better immune function and fewer upper respiratory infestions.[15] Keep this in mind when treating someone who is taking care of a sick relative. Make sure that they are well connected outside of the home.

In the realm of connection and immunologic bolstering, one can easily turn to the role of group support and its effect on cancer survival in the studies cited above, because immune surveillance is a key mechanism in cancer survival. This may be one of the contributing factors to the breast cancer and melanoma studies cited earlier. There have also been studies showing direct linkage of connection and immune function.

Can social connection impact rates of common diseases? Why do some people get colds when exposed to virons and others don't? In a study of 276 healthy volunteers, doses of inter-nasal rhinoviruses were given until the participant shed virons. The individuals were questioned on twelve types of relationships, such as with parents, children, friends, and groups. Each positive relationship was scored as one point. Participants with less than three points developed cold symptoms at a rate four times greater than those with higher scores.[16]

There have also been studies showing that massage improves immune function in AIDS patients and that modalities such as group support are effective in autoimmune diseases therapy.

Connection from the Outside In

It is not clear what causes the previously outlined benefits of interpersonal relationships. One study cited above showed that men at risk of coronary disease had lower risk if they perceived that they were loved by their spouses. Could perception be the key element of this effect? McClelland and Kershnit conducted a study that linked perception to physiology. In this study a group of students viewed one of two films; the first film depicted the extraordinary work of Mother Teresa and her order, and the other was designed to be emotionally neutral. The second task given to the students was to write a story about a photograph. The photo showed a man and woman on a park bench together.

Before and after the films were shown, salivary IgA was measured in each student. On average, the students shown the neutral film had no change in IgA levels. The students shown the film of Mother Teresa had increased levels of IgA. Most importantly, a subset of the second group showed a decrease in IgA.

The researchers then evaluated the stories written about the couple. The students who had a decrease in IgA while watching the Mother Teresa film had themes of distrust, loss, and manipulation in their stories. The students showing increased IgA had themes of love and compassion in their stories. When subsequently asked about the Mother Teresa film, the group that showed decreased IgA described negative feelings toward Mother Teresa, responding that she was a publicity seeker or asking, "Why does she get all the attention? Other people do good things too."

This demonstrates the likelihood that the effects of connection are at least partly based in perception and projection toward or onto another. In addition, attitude of perception was consistent; those students who reacted negatively toward Mother Teresa also had projected negativity onto the picture of the couple.[17]

Connection from the Inside Out
If the beneficial effect of connection is at least partly generated internally, by our perception, what models exist that might explain this? HeartMath has done a nice

job of explaining not only the internal mechanics of perceived connection but possibly also the role of human interconnectedness.[18]

It is reasonable to describe perception as the interpretation of external input to the mind-body. Neurologically, rudimentary interpretation occurs in the midbrain. It seems that the first level of this process occurs in the amygdala. The amygdala responds to this information and is responsible for the rapidity of the fight-or-flight response. The body therefore can respond in a nearly instantaneous fashion (jump!) to a harmful external stimulus. As the sympathetic neurohormonal response occurs before the neocortex is involved, the midbrain must be interpreting the stimulus as potentially harmful. The information is subsequently sent to the neocortex for analysis (e.g., "If I move seven feet to my right, I won't be hit by that two-ton red Dodge truck.").

The next step in this model, validated by animal and human research, is that the limbic system sends information to the ganglia in and around the heart via the vagus nerve. The heart has not only afferent and efferent vagal neurons but also ganglia and local-circuit, or processing, neurons.[19] These local-circuit neurons process the information and feed back to the midbrain via vagal efferents.

An additional form of language this feedback takes is HRV patterning. Over time, it forms rhythmic (high variability) or dysrhythmic (low variability) patterns. These patterns are fed back to the midbrain and, grossly, either inhibit or disinhibit midbrain and neocortical function.

This has other neurohormonal effects in the realm of autonomic and behavioral responses. For example, dysrhythmic HRV patterning caused by atrial arrhythmias has been shown to elicit panic attacks in individuals prone to panic disorder. It is usually thought to work the other way around; panic triggers elevated catecholamines, which then trigger arrythmias. In this study, 55 percent of panic attacks were preceded by the arrhythmia.[19] An interpretation of this finding is that the midbrain senses a problem with the heart and has a nonspecific fight-or-flight response. This triggers a sense of panic in these patients.

What does all of this have to do with connection? HRV patterning during a state of emotional fear, anger, or hostility is also very erratic (low variability). This has a similar effect on the midbrain, causing a fight-or-flight response. Therefore, when you are in one of these states toward another person, your internal milieu changes. Conversely a state of appreciation, love, or connection toward another person creates a very specific HRV pattern. The pattern in this case is rhythmic and predictable (in HeartMath terminology, high variability or cohesive).

When an individual is in this cohesive pattern, there are many physiologic outcomes, including improvements in blood pressure,[21] decreased cortisol, and increased DHEA,[22] as well as improved HbA1c in type II diabetics.[23] There are also many psychological changes,[18] such as decreased depression, anxiety, and hostility, as well as improved communication and cortical reactivity.

Based on the above model and data, it is reasonable to presume that appreciation of, love for, or a sense of connection with another person has positive health implications, mediated through improved neurohormonal and cardiac parameters.

The Energetics of Interconnection

If appreciation of another person can affect your own health, might this impact the other person in the relationship? Much of what is described below is of a theoretical nature, yet the potential for research and the implication make it intriguing nonetheless (and fun to think about for us science nerds). Let's look at the pieces of the science that have been demonstrated to date:

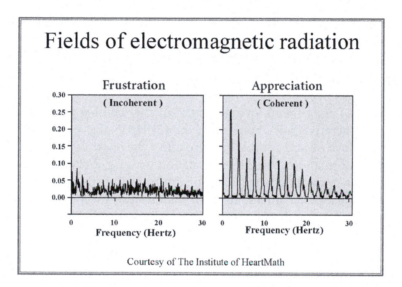

Courtesy of The Institute of HeartMath

Using the aforementioned model (HRV and physiological changes), McCraty has measured radiated electromagnetic (EM) fields of people in various emotional states. These fields can be detected about eight feet away from an individual, and should be measured in an electrically "quiet" environment. Individuals who are angry or frustrated show an electromagnetic field in disarray. The radiation has no consistent pattern. However, in the state of appreciation or love toward another, the EM field takes on a very organized, coherent pattern (see www. heartmath.org). Many of us experience another's "vibes." Is it possible that vibes are actually EM pattern differences that we are detecting?

Effect of Touch McCraty has also demonstrated that, when two people are touching, the EKG of person A is detected in the EEG of person B even when the direct conduction of signal is averaged out, meaning that one person's EKG has the opportunity to affect another's EEG patterning (see www.heartmath.org).

EKG and EEG Karl Prebram, at Stanford, has shown that EKG patterning reflecting a cohesive HRV pattern increases alpha-wave prevalence in the EEG. This means that an EM pattern from one person's EKG may be able to impact the EEG of another, therefore causing an interpersonal effect. Is mood contagious?

Change without touch Russek and Schwartz have also demonstrated this occurrence and have shown that two individuals sitting in close proximity to each other in an electrically isolated environment can exert an interpersonal effect on each other.[24] In that study, person A's EKG and person B's EKG began to sync up, without physical contact. Within a few minutes in the room together, the individuals' EKG patterns began to have a similar rate and rhythm. This means that two people can affect each other's physiologic function.

Through research on women living in dormitories, we know this to be true on a pheromone level. Isn't it reasonable to assume that there are other forms of connection and interaction, and that this type of synchronization can have health ramifications? The ramifications may be substantial in couples that sleep together over many years.

Theoretically if (1) one person's loving energy can alter another person's EKG patterning and, therefore, HRV patterning; and (2) HRV affects physiology; then (3) one person's love toward another can also affect the physiology and health of the second! If this information is used in conjunction with Dr. Prebram's findings that HRV affects brain-wave function, is it reasonable to assume that, without contact, not only can we affect each other's physiology but we can affect each other's moods and thoughts? This makes for interesting discussion, to say the least!

Many of us have had this experience with a loved one. When your mood is good and the other person's is not, you both come to a middle ground: your elation is diminished, and your loved one's mood is improved. Could have reached a co-resonant electrical patter, in the same way that two tuning forks reach a co-resonant pattern with the interactions of sound waves? How then might we be affecting our patients when we are in a bad mood or when we are not well physically? This is interesting indeed.

I state this in the realm of possibility. However, it certainly helps explain the outcomes in multiple research trials regarding community, love, connection, and healing touch.

We are not held back by the love we didn't receive in the past, but by the love we're not extending in the present.

— Marianne Williamson

CHAPTER 13 **Connection and Communication**

If you listen to the patient, they will tell you the diagnosis

— Medical professors everywhere

We all know the above statement to be true and yet we interrupt our patients within the first eighteen to twenty-two seconds of our interaction (in recorded interview studies). How then can we make a diagnosis?

Most surveys show that because we are people who enjoy connecting with others, the power of connecting with patients energizes us. So, why not do something that makes us better diagnosticians and gives us satisfaction? Time is often the excuse, but true connection takes very little time and saves you time later on.

The best way to connect is to be present, not just physically but mentally and emotionally. Bring your true self into the room. When you sit with one patient and are thinking of another patient or problem, you serve neither patient. Each distracts you from the other. Therefore you can be annoyed and dysfunctional with two patients simultaneously. Why not focus on one issue at a time? This will enhance your outcomes and efficiency, while decreasing aggravation.

Listening with Empathy
(A Maintenance and Crisis Tool — Situation Dependent)

Connecting with patients, family, and friends by empathizing gives people a sense of your concern without pretense. It is easy, because it directly accesses your emotions and, therefore, comes from your heart. It also helps you generate the greatest sense of knowing someone in the shortest period. The instruction is deceptively simple. When you are listening to someone and struggling to connect, ask yourself, "How would I feel if I was in this situation?" If you are still struggling, try to remember a time in your life when you may have felt the same way. The goal is to access a true emotion. With practice you will find that this gets you into the room with the person on an inter-human level.

Can some of these emotions be painful? Of course they can be, but isn't it better to feel both good and bad emotions than to stuff negative feelings to the point of becoming dissociated and numb? Also remember, if it is too intense, you can close down the empathy a little to protect yourself. You may need to do this when hearing a story of abuse or tragedy. It is important to remember that you are in control and that feeling and experiencing another's pain is not only reasonable but healthy for the two of you.

The best time to empathetically connect with a patient is when you like the person or want to understand them better. It is difficult to use empathy when you don't like someone, but here it can improve the relationship. When you are physically fatigued, it may also be difficult to use empathy. At all other times it is a great tool.

Patients also get better if you connect directly with them. When you make a true interpersonal connection with them, they sense that you care about and understand them. At that point they are more likely to listen to your advice. When connecting, you stand a better chance of coming up with a treatment plan that is realistic and fits the individual, instead of a cookie-cutter treatment.

It has been demonstrated that physicians who use a partnership decision model of care and communication that connects with the patient achieve better outcomes in patient anxiety, symptom improvement, patient function, blood pressure control, glucose control, and pain control.[1]

Physicians who work this way also have fewer malpractice suits and 50 percent less patient turnover.[2] So in this regard, a stronger sense of partnership and connection with our patients leads to improved clinical outcomes and better business.

Physician-Patient Relationship Levels
The clinician and patient can have three levels of interaction. This has been well documented in the dental literature, and is completely applicable to physician relationships as well. The following relationship descriptions are from Ruth Freeman.[3]

The Real Relationship
The real relationship is an equal and unique relationship between two adults. This is a genuine and realistic interaction in which the uniqueness of the physician is complemented by the uniqueness of the patient. The interaction between them therefore has a distinction that belongs only to that specific patient who interacts with that particular practitioner. Within the adult-to-adult equality of the relationship, the patient will have chosen the physician because of his or her clinical attributes and skills. In this regard, the real relationship remains unaffected by any anxieties or concerns the patient may have about treatment.

The Treatment Alliance
The treatment alliance is an equal relationship between two adults. However, while it possesses the same status equality of the real relationship, it differs. The treatment alliance is not only a development of the real relationship but is affected by the patient's anxieties and concerns about accepting treatment. For the first time in the clinician-patient relationship, the patient's concerns and anxiety about treatment seem to merge with the physician's clinical and patient management

skills. It is suggested that such barriers to compliance as phobias and costs act within the treatment alliance to distort the relationship between the physician and patient. For instance, the intensity of anxiety may render it impossible for the patient to depend upon, or align himself with, the physician. The patient may then be unable to accept or use the treatment offered by the physician.

Transference

Transference is quite distinct in its relationship characteristics but nevertheless inextricably linked to other aspects of the psychodynamic model. Like the treatment alliance, the transference develops with time, but unlike the real relationship or the treatment alliance, this is not an interaction between adults. The transference represents the past. It is a repetition of previously emotionally important relationships that are inappropriately imposed by the patient upon the physician. Therefore, as the transference represents the past, it sometimes becomes intrinsically associated with regression.

Regression simply describes the psychological state of a patient who changes from a controlled to a less-controlled emotional state. Regression is associated with a change in relationship status. The interaction is no longer one of equality between adults but one between the physician as "parent" and patient as "child." Within the transference the adult patient will reexperience childhood memories and fears, which, since they have become distorted with time, are experienced as occurring in the present. Therefore, the physician may be perceived as a caring parent, whereas, for other patients, the same physician may represent a powerful adult with the ability to cause fear or to harm.

The issue of transference is particularly important in the management of anxious patients since, for them, previous medical experiences are relived as if they were occurring in the here and now.

Equality

Time and behavioral management improve when equality and the real relationship with the patient are maintained. The patient is less anxious, the doctor is less anxious, and both patient and doctor can get to the issues at hand in a shorter time frame. You also maintain and enhance awareness of patients' concerns and anxieties as you connect with them on a human-to-human level without pretense. Interestingly when the real relationship is maintained, you are more likely to be flexible and creative in arriving at treatment plans for the patient, which is clearly a win-win situation for you and your patient.

When you reflect on the neurophysiology of this interaction, apparently if you are calm, you increase your cortical function by decreasing your catecholamines, thus becoming a better teacher. Simultaneously your calm will relax your patients, thus making them better students.

Listening with Appreciation
(A Maintenance and Crisis Tool)

By now, you've practiced shifting your breathing and activating positive emotions. We are going to apply this to communication. With your next patient visit, before going into the exam room, take a few moments to breathe deeply three or four times, then drop your attention into your heart by thinking of something you truly appreciate about the patient. If you don't really know or like that person, think of something in your life that is going well for you, and hold the sense of appreciation while going into the room. Attempt to stay in that appreciative mind-set when with the patient. At this point, listen to what your intuition tells you about the person. What really might be going on?

In many ways, this is an intuition-training skill. The more you practice, the more your intuition will be attuned and the more creative you will become. All I can say is practice, practice, practice. If it doesn't work for your intuition, you are at least lowering your catecholamines levels by doing this — not a bad side effect! Practice this simple, yet effective, technique at home as well.

A cardiologist friend of mine had an interesting outcome in doing this practice. There was a particular patient who, now five years post-MI, continued to smoke and only took his medications sporadically. Every time the cardiologist saw him, he would get agitated. Even seeing the patient's name on the schedule caused a bump in the doctor's catecholamines.

My friend wanted to take back control of his physiologic response to this guy. On his next visit, before going into the exam room, my friend shifted his breathing and focused on a feeling of love and pride for his daughter (shift and activate). He then went in the room and asked the patient about his smoking. After a bit of dancing around the subject, the patient admitted that he still smoked. My friend said that he felt his catecholamines rise and quickly shifted and activated (yes, with practice you can do this with your eyes open). At that moment he said to the patient, "I really would like you to quit smoking, but you don't seem to be ready. When you are ready, let me know and I can help you. Until then, I don't want to talk about it anymore." The patient was shocked, but agreed. My friend felt relieved.

My friend then asked the patient if he needed any more beta blockers, to which the patient responded, "No, Doc, I have plenty." Knowing that he should have been out of them by now, my friend again felt his catecholamines rise, so he shifted and activated. He then asked the patient why he didn't take his meds. The patient told him that he often went out with his buddies after work and never brought his meds with him. (Catecholamine rise, shift and activate.) My friend then calmly said, "Why don't you put your pills in the plastic wrapping of your cigarette pack so you don't forget them?" The patent was stunned, and my friend stunned himself, but the patient said, "Okay, Doc."

Many years later, the patient now takes his medication regularly but still smokes. My friend feels good because he "met the patient where he was," and no longer gets agitated when he sees the patient.

Emotional Intelligence in Medicine

In his book *Emotional Intelligence,* Daniel Goleman describes successful people as those who have both a high IQ and a high emotional intelligence. If you look at people who are successful (however you define success) they are often those who manage their emotions well, trust their intuition, and have the will to proceed despite adversity. It is clearly not just cognitive intellect that they are using.

In the book *The HeartMath Solution,* Childre and Martin describe emotional intelligence as being heart based. Although we don't think of the heart anatomically as a thinking organ, metaphorically and historically we describe it as such. Thus, true intelligence lies with a balanced use of the heart and the head, or intuition and knowledge.

In our medical lives we often use emotional detachment to provide competent service to our patients. However, for our patients, a trip to our office is always emotionally charged. This immediately creates a sense of disconnection for us from our patients, as in the treatment alliance described above. This disconnect can create fear or anger for our patient. Neither of these emotions is our intent, nor will they help the patient manage their ill health. In fact, sometimes what the patient needs is hand holding and true emotional connection. Caring must be consciously inserted into the process of engaging with a patient.

Spiritual Connection

Spirituality can be defined in many ways. For the purpose of this book, I will define spirituality as a sense of connection with something greater than oneself, such as family, friends, patients, staff, community, and religion.

Spirituality and religious practice affect our well-being. In Erica Frank's study of women physicians, those who had religious and spiritual content in their lives were happier in their work lives. I encourage you to reconnect with your family, friends, religion, and sense of a spiritual life! If you've not had a sense of spirituality in your life, I encourage you to explore this exciting and satisfying area of human existence. As someone who grew up with a rather limited religious background, devoid of spiritual content, meditation (as addressed in the next chapter) became my doorway to this wonderful and rich area of life.

CHAPTER 14 **Meditation**

As described earlier in the book, physicians like their quiet time, yet most of us get very little quiet on a day-to-day basis. Our stress accumulates for many months and then we go on a weeklong vacation. On vacation we begin to find problems: the rooms are too small, the TV is too small, the pool is too crowded, the restaurant is overbooked. We get agitated and say things to our family or the hotel staff that we regret later. Then we yell at someone. By day three or four of vacation, we start to relax and enjoy the vacation even though it's now half over. Meditation is a daily, mini-vacation that allows you to maintain sanity and emotional intelligence throughout the year and to enjoy your time off when you get some.

What if there was a product out there that allowed you, in twenty minutes, to prevent the vacation blowup, improve your sleep and your blood pressure, and enhance the fun aspects of your life? How much would you pay for it? Meditation is that product and it is free. You do not need equipment, accessories, or fancy chairs, just a quiet place to sit and twenty minutes of your time each day for meditation to do its magic. Aren't you worth it?

Meditation is the ultimate maintenance tool. However, it will require practice!

To some of you, meditation may feel like a foreign concept. Have you ever sat quietly on a beach, hypnotized by the waves? Have you ever walked in the woods and heard the sound of the trees, momentarily forgetting your thoughts? Have you ever played music or gardened and suddenly realized that, just for a moment, you had forgotten where and who you were? Have you ever prayed and felt a sense of connection with something bigger than yourself? These are meditative moments, moments when your thoughts are quiet enough that you are just you, alone and in peace. In the language of psychology these are transpersonal moments. In the language of religion you are connecting with God or spirit.

Some may believe that meditation is a way to escape reality. We've all seen people who learn meditation or go to retreats and come back sounding a bit flaky. What's up with that? Are these people ignoring the reality of the world? Can they function anymore in the real world? If you've ever sat and prayed, you've meditated. If you've ever sat on the beach breathing to the rhythm of the waves, you've meditated. If you've ever felt full of love just watching your child sleeping, you've meditated. It is unlikely that this made you flakier, but it probably gave you a sense of peace, relaxation, or love. That's meditation!

Meditation is focus. With meditation, you diminish the internal noise in your system. It is a mini-vacation each day. Like meditation, exercise and hobbies do these things as well. The difference is that, due to the depth of focus, meditation has a greater neurophysiological effect than other techniques; it gives you more bang for your buck.

The Relaxation Spectrum

Somewhat Relaxed · · · Highly Relaxed

⟵————————————————————————————⟶

Exercise   Hobbies   Reading   Music   Listening   Tai Chi   Yoga   Meditation

What is the precise definition of meditation? A medical or scientific answer might be this: a technique (or series of techniques) used to quiet cortical and midbrain activity sufficiently to allow better neurological processing. A spiritual answer might sound like this: meditation is a practice in which individuals become quiet enough to have awareness of life around them and a sense of oneness or likeness with all beings. Both answers are correct because meditation affects our neurophysiology, psychology, and spirituality.

An oft-used analogy to describe meditation compares the mind to a lake. When we're born, this lake is perfectly still. Babies' midbrains have not yet acquired all the turbulence of an adult brain, such as the stories, the defense mechanisms, or the ego. The baby's lake is still clear. This is apparent to us when we see a baby. Internally, we recall that time in our lives when we were unencumbered by internal noise. For that moment we are babies again and it feels great. All we feel is calm and loving (unless we need a diaper change).

As before, we will use the model of the midbrain as the basic processing center of emotion. Seeing a baby stimulates the memory of nurturing and thus creates a physiologic response of that emotion in the form of calmness or peacefulness. We breathe in deeply, sigh, and relax automatically. Our catecholamines decrease, our sympathetic tone decreases, our cortisol levels drop, and other positive changes occur. This is akin to the results of meditation.

Our midbrains are more experienced in the realm of fear and self-protection, yet have the capacity to feel calm, nurtured, and loving. Meditation is a way to enhance that activity in our midbrains. As Pavlov did with his dogs, our midbrains can be trained to respond this way to previously perceived adverse circumstances. The more you practice, the more likely you are to see things in the way a calm and unhindered person would.

Goals of Meditation
There are many varied goals of meditation, dependent on what the individual hopes to achieve. Meditation can help improve cortical function, so it can be

very helpful to enhance creativity, mental clarity, learning, and listening. In this way it can also improve athletic performance. If cortical function speeds up, then the rest of the world appears to slow down. This becomes a very useful goal on a basketball court to slow the game down. Many coaches and athletes use meditation.

In the language of transpersonal psychology, meditation can help you re-perspective your own reality and learn to accept the reality of others. It helps you gain a sense of enhanced consciousness and connection with the universal consciousness. This leads to mood changes of greater serenity and joy, as well as increased vitality. Meditation will also increase your capacity to love and connect with others.

Meditation has also been applied in the medical training arena. In one such example, an eight-week meditation-training program showed significant reductions in medical students' anxiety and depression, as well as improved their empathy levels.[1] In another study of medical students participating in a ten-week meditation program, the meditation group (compared to controls) scored significantly lower in the total mood-disturbance scale at the completion of the intervention period. Significant effects were also observed on tension-anxiety, confusion-bewilderment, fatigue-inertia, and vigor-activity subscales.[1,2]

In total, there have been twenty-four intervention studies using meditation-like techniques with medical trainees, both students and residents, with the following results:[3]

- Improved immunologic functioning
- Decreases in depression and anxiety
- Increased spirituality and empathy
- Enhanced knowledge of alternative therapies for future referrals
- Improved knowledge of the effects of stress
- Greater use of positive coping skills
- An enhanced ability to resolve role conflicts

In the Buddhist philosophy, meditation is described as a way to help you to decrease suffering. Suffering is described as a lack of contentment or peace. According to Cheri Huber, a nurse and meditation teacher, the four basic causes of suffering are (1) not getting what you want, (2) getting what you want and not being satisfied with it, (3) having to endure the absence of someone or something you love, (4) and having to endure the presence of someone or something you do not love.[4]

Meditation also helps you to accept who you are and care for yourself more lovingly, stop judging others and accept who they are, and stop comparing yourself to others. These are very common issues for those in medicine.

The Physiological and Clinical Effects of Meditation

A multitude of studies have been done looking at the physiological and clinical effects of meditation and similar practices of self-regulatory techniques. Here, I will review some of the literature on the physiologic effects of meditative practices.

When comparing non-meditators, short-term meditators, and meditators practicing for at least one year, the long-term meditators had increased vital capacity tidal volume and the ability to hold the breath longer, as well as lower resting heart rates. Meditators also had lower total and LDL cholesterol values.[5]

In a randomized, controlled, single-blind trial with three months of follow-up in a primary-care inner-city health center, older African Americans with mild hypertension were taught meditation and the body scan (introduced in this chapter) as stress-reduction approaches. These were compared with a lifestyle-modification education control program and with each other to evaluate the effects on blood pressure.

Meditation reduced systolic pressure by 10.7 mm Hg (P < .0003) and diastolic pressure by 6.4 mm Hg (P < .00005). Progressive muscle relaxation (body scan) lowered systolic pressure by 4.7 mm Hg (P = 0.0054) and diastolic pressure by 3.3 mm Hg (P < .02). The reductions in the Transcendental Meditation (also known as TM) group were significantly greater than in the progressive muscle relaxation group for both systolic blood pressure (P = .02) and diastolic blood pressure (P = .03).[6]

The effect of meditation on blood pressure may be due to multiple physiological changes. In individuals practicing a daily twenty to thirty minute meditation, renin activity, aldosterone levels, and cortisol levels decline within a few months. This does not occur with an equivalent time spent in quiet rest with your eyes closed.[7] Twenty minutes of meditation also decreases total peripheral resistance in middle-aged adults when compared to eyes-open or eyes-shut rest.[8] These effects may partially explain the benefit of meditation in hypertension. The difference between just resting and practicing meditation is that meditation is an active process, directed toward quieting the mind.

In addition to hypertension management, meditation appears to have other benefits in cardiac risk reduction. In a study of individuals with ischemic heart disease who demonstrated ischemia with mental stress, meditation had a significant mortality impact. This study was based on previous studies showing that mental stress can induce cardiac ischemia. The theory was that this mental-stress induced ischemia could be blocked or diminished through meditation.

One hundred and seven patients with CAD and ischemia were observed during mental-stress testing or ambulatory electrocardiographic monitoring and were randomly assigned to a four-month program of exercise or stress management training. Myocardial ischemia patients or their surviving families were reassessed following treatment for up to five years to document cardiac events, including death, nonfatal myocardial infarction, and cardiac revascularization procedures.

In this trial, meditation had a more powerful effect on cardiac outcomes than exercise training in the five-year period. This is likely due to the fact that meditation helps shift perspective and enhances self-care. The meditation subjects ate healthier and exercised more than the other groups, even though they had no training in these areas. Exercise only works when one is also meditating.[9]

Other mechanisms by which meditation may affect cardiovascular health have been demonstrated. When used in a population of African American men, considered by ultrasound to have significantly increased carotid intimal thickness, meditation showed a reduction of intimal thickness within six months without any other interventions.[10]

Meditation affects various mood states and neurochemical states. In healthy volunteers, meditation caused significant increases in left-sided anterior brain activation, a pattern associated with positive effect. Simultaneously it caused increases in antibody titers to influenza vaccine. The magnitude of increase in left-sided activation predicted the magnitude of antibody-titer rise to the vaccine.[11]

In healthy volunteers, an additional effect on brain function was a 22 percent decrease in reaction time after meditation practice; showing dramatic improvement of cortical function. The changes in reaction time are particularly interesting in that meditation has been shown to enhance sport and academic performance. Improved reaction time may be one of the ways in which this occurs.[12]

In patients with *DSM-IV*–defined anxiety disorders, meditation has a significant impact on the subjective and objective symptoms of anxiety and panic. This improvement persisted over three years of follow-up.[13]

Diminished anxiety might partially account for meditation's effects in improving sleep in patients with breast cancer,[14] and mood and quality of life of prostate cancer patients as well as patients with other cancers.[15, 16] In fact meditation improved the quality of life in all individuals in an outpatient environment, showing a 28 percent reduction in physical symptoms of all sorts, as well as a significant reduction in psychological distress and anxiety, and a 34 percent reduction in depression. These effects are maintained over time as well.[17]Meditation affects the clinical experience of patients with many disorders. It is particularly logical that it would be an effective therapy in disorders clearly affected by stress hormones. This is true for irritable bowel syndrome, showing significant reduction in abdominal pain, diarrhea, flatulence, and bloating.[18]

Chronic-pain patients also benefit greatly from meditation. The reduction of catecholamines probably contributes to this effect by decreasing muscle spasticity.

In addition the mood-elevating effects of meditation surely help this population. In one such study, negative body image and inhibition of activity by pain, symptoms, mood disturbance, and psychological symptomatology, including anxiety and depression, were improved with a twenty-minute daily meditation practice over a ten-week period, and sustained for fifteen months post-training.[19]

As you can see, the potential benefits of a daily meditation practice are huge and obtainable with a time commitment of twenty minutes each day. The remainder of this chapter has fun imageries and meditations for you to use.

Reading about meditation doesn't decrease your blood pressure, improve your cognitive function, improve your performance, and shift your mood; so just do it! You may want to buy a guided meditation CD to get you going (I offer some on my Web site: www.findingbalanceproductions.com). For a start, I will give you some simple, fun meditations to do.

As meditation is an experience-based practice, this section will have multiple styles of meditations. Try each of them a few times to get the feel for them and see which has the most appeal. If you enjoy them, you are more likely to practice them.

Meditation Exercise — Food
(Five-Minute Tool)

We will start by simply concentrating on a raisin. This shows us how, through increased focus, we can get a deeper experience out of a simple pleasure.

Get a raisin. If you dislike raisins, start with another small piece of dried fruit. Sit in a comfortable chair, and go through the following steps:

1. Study the raisin. Pretend that this a scientific field expedition and you just discovered this previously undocumented object.
2. Write down a description of the object. Pretend that you never saw this type of object before.
3. Draw a picture of the object as if you were documenting it for the world's scientific community.
4. Next, smell the raisin for subtle scents (as you would do in a wine tasting) . Write down what you smell.
5. Now place the raisin between your molars, toward the back. Pay attention to what happens. Document the response.
6. Now bite down once and roll the raisin around in your mouth, eventually bringing it back to the molars. Do not swallow the raisin. Write down what flavors you taste.
7. Next, chew up the raisin slowly and completely, and roll it around on your tongue. Close your eyes and swallow.

What was this like? Did you experience that raisin differently than others you've had?

When we slow down and study an experience using our mind and sensations, the experience grows in magnitude. This is meditation. It is the focus on one object to truly experience it and distract you from other thoughts. Try this with other foods or sensory experiences. I'll leave the rest to you.

Meditation on the Body — Body Scan
(Two to Ten-Minute Tool)

This is a simple, effective maintenance tool that takes two to ten minutes.
The body scan is a quick technique to diminish stress. It is really useful when you are trying to sleep or when you are getting tired in the office. This technique can be used for relaxing and for enhancing cortical function. Do it as slowly or quickly as you desire.

Find a comfortable position, seated or lying down. Most prefer lying down.

Uncross your legs and arms; let them be supported by the ground or chair and floor.

Close your eyes, if this is comfortable (may be done with eyes open).

Begin to feel your breath coming in and out of your body. Feel it enter your nose or mouth, move past your airways, and fill your lungs. Feel it moving in the reverse direction. Pay attention to your breath for a while.

Now bring your focus to your toes as you continue breathing slowly and deeply. Wiggle your toes slightly and focus your attention on them.

Now bring your attention to the soles of your feet as you continue to breathe deeply.

Now bring your attention to your calves.

Now bring your attention to your knees; move them gently.

Now bring your attention to your thighs; move them. Tense and relax them as you continue to breathe deeply.

Now bring your attention to your buttocks; squeeze them together.

Now bring your attention to your low back. Notice any pain or tightness there. Breathe deeply through this area and let the muscles relax.

Now bring your attention to your stomach. Pay attention to its movement as you breathe in and out.

Now bring your attention to your chest. Pay attention to its movement as you breathe in and out.

Now bring your attention to your shoulders. Feel for any tension there and release it with your breath.

Now bring your attention to your neck. Roll it gently side to side and relax the muscles.

Now bring your attention to your facial muscles. Feel for any tension there and let it go.

Now bring your attention to your head and hair. Feel the air moving around your head. Continue breathing and release all of your body's tension.

Meditation on a Visual Focus
(Ten-Minute Tool)

The following meditation is adapted from Nischala Joy Devi.[20]

Light a candle on a table. Ideally, lower or shut off the room lights. We will use the candle flame as a point of focus.

Find a comfortable seated position. Ideally your spine should be erect. If you're in a chair, place your feet flatly on the floor. If you can't do this, place a pillow, stool, or block under your feet so that they are resting flatly.

Take a moment to stretch your back, roll your neck and shoulders, and get comfortable. Place your hands palms-down on your legs, or if you're comfortable, place them palms-up, one atop the other, in your lap. Just relax and see how your body feels.

You are going to use a soft gaze for this meditation, so your eyes should remain open. In meditation, you'll notice that when your eyes are focused, the mind is focused. When your mind tends to go astray, your eyes move also.

When you practice meditation, begin with gazing. Keep your eyes focused on the candle flame. Allow your mind to go to the flame. The goal is to keep your eyes still.

Remember to sit comfortably, with your spine erect and shoulders back. Eventually you'll get in the habit so that, when you merely think about meditation, your back will straighten and your shoulders will come back. Now, just take in a few deep breaths. Inhale through your nose, and as you exhale, let that breath out very slowly, and, along with it, any tension that you feel. Take in another breath and let it out even more slowly, and feel yourself relaxing.

After closing your eyes briefly, slowly allow them to open, and begin to gaze at the image. At first, just for comfort, allow your eyes to wander to the area around your focal point. Allow them to settle on your point of focus. Keep your eyes open, but when they start to blink or feel uncomfortable, allow them to close and rest, and see that same vision in your mind. When that vision begins to fade, open your eyes again and gaze on the external object.

At times you will notice that your mind and eyes wander a bit. You may think of something you forgot to do or tell someone. This is a good sign. It means that clarity is beginning, the mental noise is decreasing, and you are starting to remember things. When this happens, make a mental note to do this task, fold the note, and put it in an imaginary "to do" box. After your meditation it will be there for you. Now bring your focus back to the focal point and breathe deeply.

As you observe the flame, notice its qualities.
(Allow two to three minutes of quiet time.)

As your eyes become tired, allow them to close, and see the flame with your inner vision. When that vision fades, once again open your eyes, gazing at the flame. Continue the process, gazing outward and inward. See if you can let all your thoughts and feelings go and just concentrate on the simplicity of the focal point. If you begin to feel any tension in your body, take in a few deep breaths and let them go.

Now close your eyes and allow that image to reflect the beauty and peace within.
(Allow two to three minutes of quiet time or as long as you'd like.)

Keeping your eyes closed, briskly rub your palms together, generating heat. Gently cup your palms over your eyes, resting your fingertips on your hairline, and just allow the darkness and warmth to penetrate deeply into and behind your eyes, soothing away any tension you feel. Very slowly bring your fingertips down and stroke your eyelids out toward your ears, once again, removing any tension or strain from your eyes. Return your hands to your lap.

Shake out your arms and legs, and move your head and shoulders. The important thing during meditation is to let go of any tension.

Meditation on a Loved One
(Ten to Twenty Minute Tool)

For our next practice, we will use an emotional focus. Most people find focusing on loved ones to be the most pleasant form of meditation. It intentionally brings the focus to the feeling of love or of being in love. It uses emotion as a focal point. This is my personal favorite, as I am a die-hard romantic. We often focus on things that cause anger; thinking of someone you love is the way to inoculate against that habit.

Generate a list of people, places, or things that help you feel loving. You'll need more than one because it is not unusual for a loved one to be the cause of your stress. Therefore if you train yourself to focus on one person, and he or she happens to be causing you stress lately, you have no place to go for relief.

Let's start with a person whom you love (who presently isn't causing you stress). Find a comfortable position and close your eyes. Take some slow, deep breaths until you feel relaxed and calm.

Visualize the person you love or appreciate. See yourself with that person in a special place. What do you see there? Are you sitting or standing? Can you feel the ground beneath your feet or the place where you are sitting? Try feeling the air. What does it feel like? Are there any smells that you can identify?

Now focus on the person you're with. Focus on your appreciation and love for that person. In your mind, tell your loved one how much you love and appreciate him or her. Hear what your loved one says back to you, if anything.

Be with the person and admire him or her as you would a great piece of art. Thank your loved one for being in your life. If your mind wanders, bring your focus back to this person or someone else you love.

You may want to walk together in a favorite place. If so, feel the ground beneath your feet. Smell and feel the air around you. Listen for any sounds you might hear. Enjoy the place and whomever you are with.

When you are ready, say thank you and good-bye to your partner, and bring your mind back to the room.

By giving yourself this experience, you have altered your physiology as if you had really been there.

I shut my eyes in order to see.

— Paul Gauguin

Meditation on Breath
(Ten to Twenty Minute Tool)

Breath is life. This is obvious to us clinicians. The gas exchange that occurs with respiration is necessary for survival, but in many ways it is the way that we become part of everything. Plants produce the oxygen we need. The CO_2 and nitrogen we inhale will become part of other people's bodies because the CO_2 we produce will go in and out of countless others over the next millennium. It will also supply plants with the basis of their existence. At any given time, you will breathe in and incorporate molecules that were once part of Jesus, Buddha, Albert Einstein, or John F. Kennedy. There is no escaping the universality of this experience.

Using the breath to meditate is something that is very rhythmical. It's very much like the ocean tide. The waves come in and the waves go out. Many of us have sat for hours watching that — in and out — and so goes the breath of life. Focusing on the breath affirms the life as it comes in and becomes part of us.

The rhythm of breathing helps balance the autonomic nervous system through various reflex cycles. While enhancing oxygenation, it also slows heart rate and decreases muscle tone. As with gazing, it also gives you something to focus on and thus calms the midbrain output.

Take a comfortable seated position. Place your arms in a comfortable position. Close your eyes. Bring your awareness to your breath. It comes in and goes out through your nose. Watch it as you would the waves of the ocean coming in and going out.

Now, notice that as you breathe in, the air is slightly cool. As you exhale, the air is warmer. Feel both temperatures through your nostrils, the cool and the warm. Just begin to observe the coolness and the warmth as it comes and goes without controlling the breath in any way. Merely observe how it flows in and out, as the tide does, as do the gentle waves coming onto the shore, without any hesitation. As it comes in, it gently rolls out.

If your mind begins to wander from your breath, gently bring it back to the flow, in and out. Notice how the rest of your body feels. Is there tension? Gently in, gently out. (Allow one minute of quiet time.)

As you breathe in and out, feel the air traveling down your trachea and into your lungs. Can you feel the air entering and then leaving each of your lung lobes? Pay attention to this for a few minutes.

If you start to lose the sensitivity of your breath, breathe in a little deeper, and feel that coolness once again.

Begin to feel the chest as it rises and falls, and the belly as it moves in and out. The whole system seems to move in rhythm with the breath. You may even find a slight smile coming to your face as your body and mind relax, and as you touch that inner place of peace and calm. Stay in this relaxed place as long as you desire.

Then, very slowly, without moving the body at all, let your eyes open just slightly. As you feel ready, very slowly move your head and neck, followed by your arms and legs.

Building a Meditation Habit

I suggest a practice of five to ten minutes daily to start. Use whichever meditation works best for you. You can do this in the morning, evening, or both. After two weeks, increase your time by five minutes. Continue this until you are meditating twenty minutes daily. This is when the long-term physiologic shifts occur, according to the research on meditation.

Meditation is a very unusual and somewhat difficult practice for many people. In our society we are not in any way rewarded or even encouraged for being still. I don't know how many of you, when you were children, were told to stop daydreaming and pay attention. Many of us feel that our meditation comes in the form of reading a paper or watching TV. To learn as adults to begin to cultivate the idea of being still, quiet, and meditative is very difficult. Don't get discouraged; it takes time.

At some point you may think, "Oh, I've been doing it now for two weeks and I've felt nothing." There are people who have done it for twenty or thirty years who feel the benefit but on a very subtle level. I encourage you to persevere, though you may not notice any changes right away. It's like learning a sport, a musical instrument, or even a surgical technique; at first it is awkward and difficult. When you start, you think and obsess about every step of the process. However, with continued practice, it becomes second nature, to the extent that you subconsciously use it moment to moment throughout your day. Remember, the best way to learn meditation is not by reading about it; it is by doing it.

The man who has no inner life is a slave to his surroundings.

— Henry Frederic Amiel

CHAPTER 15

Psychosynthesis

The whole is greater than the sum of its parts. This is how we describe many events, processes, and systems in the world where we live, yet do we think of ourselves as a whole composed of many parts? What if you could pick apart the various aspects of your personality then choose the one you wanted to be at any given time? This is a simple, reasonable description of the rationale and techniques of psychosynthesis. Psychosynthesis looks at the personality as a whole composed of multiple smaller parts, or sub-personalities.

Italian psychotherapist Roberto Assagioli, MD, first described this model of psychotherapy in the 1920s. He observed that psychoanalytic psychotherapy was a process of getting rid of the unwanted past. He noticed that individuals who were in psychological dysfunction or had a sense of meaningless tended to struggle from an inner turmoil, whereas individuals who were balanced, energetic, or empowered by meaning had little or no inner conflict.[1] Psychosynthesis is a method of self-analysis evaluating inner conflict and how it occurs, and then learning to manage it. It is about taking charge of your personality. It also will help you to manage inner conflict and to work closer to your core values.

Assagioli described what might be the source of this inner conflict or lack thereof. He postulated that we are composed of multiple sub-personalities. Each sub-personality has its own reason for being and often develops in response to external or perceived external circumstances. For example, the person you are when you are with your spouse or children is likely to be warm, caring, and nurturing, and also less likely to be decisive or dogmatic. We develop this sub-personality out of love and wanting to be loved.

As a physician, you are trained to play a different role. This role requires you to be decisive, caring, inquisitive, and, to some degree, emotionally dissociated. In this role you can manage difficult and emergent clinical scenarios, delegate appropriate responsibilities, and remain clearheaded. This is an especially desirable trait in the emergency room.

The inner conflict arises when you act as a sub-personality that is inappropriate to the situation. For example, have you ever acted as your decisive, emotionally dissociated, doctor personality at the dinner table? Your family may not want or need that part of you at that time and will often tell you so (many fights start this way). The inner conflict here is that you feel as if you are being you and that they are not accepting you for who you are. On a base level you don't feel loved and supported, and without awareness, you can wonder what's bugging them. The problem is that you are behaving as the inappropriate "you" for the moment.

Another example is a situation in which you do what you think you should do when this action conflicts with what you actually want to do. What voice is telling you what should be done? What voice is telling you what you want done? The should voice may be that of a parent or teacher that you've incorporated. The want voice may be a part of you expressing need, desire, or even rebellion against the parent or teacher. Yet, are both voices not two sides of you? They live together within you.

It is important to note that having sub-personalities is normal and usual, whereas having a multiple-personality disorder is pathological. In true multiple-personality disorder, the personalities are unaware of each other. This is truly dissociative. Sub-personalities are aware of each other and can be in active conflict, as in "should" and "want." You might think of this as associative as opposed to dissociative.

An additional way to view these sub-personalities would be from a Freudian viewpoint. Freud described these subsets as developing out of fear or pressure to adjust to situations. Early in life, this fearful situation may be separation from the mother. When this occurs, the child creates an internal "mother" to soothe himself or herself. This process is called interjection. The child then has an internal mother anytime she is needed. When a mother puts a child to bed, she will often say soothing phrases such as, "Sleep well," "Have good dreams," and "It will be light in the morning." When the mother leaves the room and the child becomes afraid, the child repeats these phrases internally as a form of self-soothing. This action interjects such phrases and the soothing attitude into the child's language and way of being. As adults with our own children, we often find ourselves using the language and attitudes of our parents in similar events to those in which we learned them. Sometimes this can be rather startling or even unwanted, if it's a behavior you didn't like in your own parent.

An interesting aspect of this theory is that the interjected personality is the child's perception of the mother. This is not necessarily the same as the mother's true personality. The soothing mother in the above example can be in a dysfunctional marriage or she can be an alcoholic or rage addict. After soothing the child, the mother could go out on a drinking binge or have a fight with her spouse. The child's interpretation and, therefore, interjection are based on only the part of the mother that they see and need.

This will also affect you later in life, when putting your own child to bed; in that moment you may reconnect with the emotionality of yourself as a child. This can lead to responses, behaviors, and defenses that make no sense within the construct of your adult personality.

The Interjected Parent
(Ten-Minute Power Tool)

I encourage you to do a written exercise to evaluate how you have or haven't interjected your parents' personalities into yourself. For each of your parents, write down as many of their personality traits as you can think of.

Write both the desirable traits and the undesirable traits. See which ones you have adopted.

In every real man, a child is hidden that wants to play.

— Friedrich Nietzsche

A commonly discussed example of a sub-personality manifesting itself is the midlife crisis. In our society, we often suppress our youthful and impulsive tendencies because they seem inappropriate for responsible grown-ups. The chronic suppression of these sub-personalities energizes them to emerge, as happens in any suppressed individual. The sub-personalities will at times break free as emotional outbursts, irrational purchases, substance abuse, or even sexual affairs. We often display these behaviors as a way of demonstrating our freedom. What we are demonstrating is an internal child who doesn't like thirty years of suppression. This can be viewed as a form of upstaging. The impulsive actor wants a bigger role in the play. Yet these actions often have devastating relationship and financial ramifications.

If we allow this independent, impulsive youth to be part of our daily life, in balance with the external grown-up that we are conditioned to display, not only will we avoid sweeping irrationalities, but we can also have more fun and feel freer! In essence all of our internal characters need understanding, compassion, and avenues of expression.

You can also view these sub-personalities as actors in a play. In this model, you are the director of the play and your life at that moment is the scene. The director then gets to choose which actor gets to play in a given scene. The goal is to avoid having the actors upstage one another or using them inappropriately in a scene.

The overall goal of psychosynthesis is to be a better director of your life's play, to have your actors feel appreciated, and to use them for their strongest roles. In this way we gain our freedom, recapture our fun, and enhance our creativity and productivity.

With this in mind Assagioli developed a multitude of tools in order to achieve a sense of freedom, control, and life benefits. These tools help you to gain enhanced awareness of your sub-personalities, so that you recognize when you are wearing your lab coat to dinner. This will help you see your role in whatever conflict arises, as opposed to immediately placing the blame on your family. These tools can allow you to consciously switch to a more appropriate sub-personality, thereby gaining greater control and comfort in the moment. They can allow you to evaluate the role of your sub-personalities in your current life. For example, the hyper-arousable resident you became in training may no longer be a valuable member of your "inner family" and may cause you to snap at others. And these tools can allow you to merge or integrate your sub-personalities too, for a greater whole or to become a well-integrated person.

In addition psychosynthesis can help you gain awareness of your sub-personalities and ways of being that are only marginally in your current awareness, so that you can respond more appropriately and be less surprised by them. Knowing what personality resources are at hand can also help you to plan better and be more proactive. By gaining this sense of control and objectivity about your personality, you can gain greater connection with the collective unconscious — the state of spiritual awareness, as described by Carl Jung. As the Buddhists would say, you become the objective observer of the self.

Likes and Dislikes
(Ten-Minute Exercise)

A good way to begin this self-analysis is to evaluate personality traits that you like. For most of us these would include integrity, honesty, creativity, humor, and other attributes. Many psychotherapists say that we like these traits because they reflect parts of us that we like about ourselves. These parts are sub-personalities. You can think of them as Mr. Integrity, Joe Honest, the Artist, and your inner Seinfeld.

Turning our focus to parts of us that we dislike, we may find Mr. Manipulative, the Boss, Judge Judy, or the Critic. Such negative sub-personalities may be part of us too, even though we don't let them show up very often. We are often agitated by the negative parts of us that we see in others. They serve as mirrors of our souls.

For me, a prime example of this occurs when a plane lands (I travel a lot) and everyone whips out their cell phones to check messages. As a type-A personality, I feel compelled to do the same thing. This makes me anxious and even mad at the others. The reality is that I am mad at myself for having this compulsion.

The naming (such as Judge Judy) of our sub-personalities is an important part of the process. Once a sub-personality has a name, you don't need to think of multiple traits to identify what it feels like to be that personality. The name alone brings them all to mind. This then will allow you to work with the personality.

In doing this work, I have come across my predominant sub-personalities. I offer them to you as examples of how this works. There is no order here. They are all part of me and can be used as needed or desired. As you will see, I tend to think of many of my own sub-personalities by what they wear.

- **The Blue Suit** – This sub-personality is one that I use when I do a medical lecture in front of large audiences. He is opinionated, clear, direct, and able to project comfortably. He works best in front of a large group of highly intelligent people. Using this personality allows me to feel confident and very organized in my thinking. This diminishes any public speaking anxieties that I might otherwise have. I actually developed this sub-personality in order to feel confident in front of large groups of physicians.

- **Flannel Shirt** – This may be the polar opposite of the Blue Suit. The Flannel Shirt is most at home in the backyard or the woods. He listens to the Grateful Dead. He plays guitar and loves to hike. He generally cannot and doesn't want to make decisions. He doesn't want to be organized. He is my chilling-out personality and works really well after having been in Blue Suit mode for a few days.

- **Sport Coat** – This is Blue Suit Lite, a softer version of the same. The major difference is that Sport Coat guy is much more open and willing to hear others' opinions. He is certainly less defensive than the Blue Suit guy. Sport Coat is the personality that I use when leading workshops or having small business meetings. He is a good team player.

- **Pajamas** – This is the "me" that snuggles on the couch with someone I love. He is soft, loving, quiet, and indecisive, and laughs freely. In this mode, "whatever" is heard a lot.

- **The Dweeb** – This sub-personality developed in school and in learning how to do research. He loves to be in the library or at the computer. He hates to be interrupted. He has a fair amount of ego and relishes his creative powers. This is the guy you need to help you find the independent variables in a clinical intervention. This is not a guy you want to be at a party with.

- **Lenny** – This is my impulsive, teen-age, sometimes troublemaking self. You can find him at the Fillmore Auditorium slam-dancing and jumping around with the other testosterone-laden people. He is a lot of fun but sometimes makes bad choices. By the way, his name is based on my dear friend Lenore, who in her troublemaking moments is Lenny's best partner.

- **Zorro** – This is the slash-and-burn version of me. He yells at Kathy and the kids and is just plain evil. He comes out when I am physically or emotionally exhausted. I used to get deeply depressed after he showed his ugly head. Now I am at one with him.

Draw a Picture of Yourself as a Doctor
(Five-Minute Exercise)

I'd like you to try something to evaluate your "doctor" self. Get a piece of blank paper and draw a picture of yourself in this role. Be honest. No one is watching and you won't be graded.

Below the picture, list the personality traits of this person? List all of them, both good and bad.

Now draw a picture of yourself doing something unrelated to medicine. What are the personality traits of this person?

Can you see how you are a different person under different circumstances?

Gaining Control

Unconsciously you already know how to choose the appropriate sub-personality for a given moment. At a party you are the "party" you. At work you are the "work" you. You may even choose your clothing for the day based on the "you" that you want to be. As you learn about your own sub-personalities, you can use them in even more directed ways.

As you begin to analyze the assets and deficits of each sub-personality, you can see how they serve you. In doing so, you can begin to modify them as needed. For example, when you need to make a decision, the clarity of Judge Judy may be very welcome and desirable. You can mentally alter her a bit so that she becomes Decisive Judy. You can do this because decisiveness is a trait that you have that can be exhibited without the judgmental nature. By understanding and analyzing the various traits of a sub-personality, as above, you can pick and choose or merge and control these traits.

How have I done this based on the sub-personalities I have shared with you? Below are a couple of examples:

- In the past, my usual grand rounds personality was more like the Sport Coat guy, but as I did more and more public speaking in stressful environments, I needed something more. I needed to be more directed and confident. I needed to be strong in my opinions. These were attributes that I already had in other parts of my life. So I took the Sport Coat guy, added a little confidence and a bit of Zorro's strength and arrogance, baked for forty minutes on high, and came up with the Blue Suit guy. He could protect me and give me confidence in a room of two-thousand opinionated colleagues. He became a very effective addition for many years. Interestingly, with age and confidence in my skills, I need him less and less. He too has softened and matured, and no longer has to be right all the time.

- What about Zorro? How could I be at peace with him? I have learned to use his aggressive energies when needed, while keeping them in my control. There are times where I need to take a clear stance and be aggressive with someone. Taming Zorro's energy allows me to do this without getting emotionally involved with the anger.

The Taming of the Shrew

When not in your control, the angry, Zorro-like characters can get you into deep trouble and make you do things that you later regret. So how can you gain control? The following steps will help you with this. I will use my Zorro character as an example, because he was the one that was most disruptive in my life. I also believe that there is a little Zorro in all of us, in the form of our angry, dark selves.

1. Identify your sub-personalities and see how they are working for you today.
2. Understand why he or she exists. When I started to evaluate Zorro's reason for being, it became very clear. He arose mostly when I was exhausted and feeling out of control. Zorro was a way to regain control and distance myself from those around me. He created a big fiery wall that I would dare others to approach.
3. Where did this come from? When I was young, my mother felt like her life was out of control in handling us kids. Her response was to rage at us.
4. How can you get your goals met in other ways? So if the goal of my Zorro personality was to regain control and create space for myself, how could I do this without doing harm? First, I had to find a way to create a wall without the fire. Having a spouse who was willing to help made a big difference. I told Kathy and the kids that I was exhausted. When a situation came up that I couldn't manage, I just asked Kathy to manage it for me. When she was unable to do this, I disappeared to my room for a while to regain control or do something physical such as work out. This allowed me the space I needed without hurting others.

What has been the outcome of this process? I now can use Zorro's energy to get things done and to lovingly be in my kids' faces (aggressively but lovingly directed). I can be bold and strong when needed. When Zorro used to show up, I would get depressed afterward. This happened because I did something bad, yelled, screamed, or broke things and felt miserable about it. I was often depressed for hours or days afterward. I was behaving like my mother when she was out of control. Here I was being the antithesis of what I strived to be. Now when Zorro shows up unwanted (and he still does now and again), I can forgive myself quickly and move on. I truly accept that he is part of me and will be around now and again, and also can be used and harnessed when needed. He no longer controls me; I control him.

Identifying Your Sub-personalities

(A Restructuring Power Tool — Thirty Minutes)

Let's now fully evaluate our sub-personalities by identifying and naming them.

Step 1: Identify Your Sub-personalities

I encourage you to get out some paper and crayons and draw some of your sub-personalities. Drawing helps to get you out of you linear mind and can inspire creativity. These sub-personalities can be based on mood states, activities, or relationships, for example, the Angry Guy, Soccer Woman, Lover. This will help you to create a list of all of your sub-personalities, as I have shown above. With each drawing, write down the specific personality traits associated with that sub-personality; for example, Judge Judy might be decisive, arrogant, clear, expressive, and critical. The Couch Potato might be lazy, quiet, relaxed, and indecisive.

Step 2: Why Do They Exist?

As you evaluate your sub-personalities, you will see that each has traits that serve you in a different part of your life. Judge Judy might be a useful character when everyone around you is unclear and indecisive. She may disserve you in your love relationships. The Couch Potato may be really useful on a Sunday morning when you don't want to think about work and just need a break, but may disserve you when work around the house needs to get done.

Every sub-personality has a purpose, even if it's not obvious to you. You wouldn't have created them had they not served you somehow. Those that come from your family of origin may be particularly difficult. They often develop as a way to identify, positively or negatively, with your parent. In the negative form, it may be that you didn't want to be like your parents, so you created a you that is the antithesis of your parents.

Step 3: Where Did They Come From?

To further understand how our sub-personalities developed, let's look at various ways of grouping their genesis. This categorization was created by Carl Jung and others. The four general groupings are as follows:

Familial Sub-personalities Familial sub-personalities arise as reflections of the birth family environment, for example, hearing a parent's voice in your head. These are our interpretations of our parents' behaviors. If you have ever caught yourself acting like one of your parents, this is the source. These sub-personalities can also be in reaction to, or rebellion against, your parents. For example, if your parents abide by all the rules and fear authority, you can develop a reckless or rebellious part of your personality that may get you into trouble. For many of us, this is how we respond to someone who tries to control our behaviors.

Societal Sub-personalities Societal sub-personalities reflect societal beliefs; for example, the man should be the breadwinner. These beliefs are constructs set up by any given society or community and vary between communities. They are certainly nothing you knew at birth.

Archetypal Sub-personalities Archetypal sub-personalities are those that occur repetitively in people, almost regardless of their familial or societal tendencies. These tend to be metaphoric in nature. Here are some examples: "I am not enough," "the Imposter," "the Dark Side," "the Good Face," and "the Controller."

Archetypal sub-personalities can also include archetypes such as Hero, Warrior, God, Goddess, or Lover. These sub-personalities cross over into many societies and communities. They are found in the world's literature and music, and occur in almost all cultures.

Anima and Animus Carl Jung described animus as the idealized man inside every woman, and anima as the idealized woman inside every man. To some degree, we all hold a male and female side and its corresponding characteristics. On a simple level, examples would include nurturing (female) or aggressive (male). At a more complex level, the anima and animus tend to be projected, or mapped, onto other people when we are not conscious of them in our own psyches. An example of this is the repressed homosexual who makes homophobic comments. Such behavior results from the unconsciously suppressed anima being projected onto someone else to divert attention away from an anxious or unaccepted part of the self.

Using the above descriptions, can you identify where your dominant sub-personalities came from? If you are struggling with this, begin to think of your parents' personality traits. How many of them have you adopted or rebelled against? It might help to list them as such to get a clearer picture.

Some of the traits that we adopt to rebel against our parents can become disruptive to our lives. A good friend of mine, Steve, is an ophthalmic surgeon. In doing this exercise, he realized that he had created a Superman sub-personality in an attempt to avoid being like his pushover father. While he described this in our workshop, his wife vigorously nodded her head in recognition of the sub-personality. Steve had always thought that Superman was a good sub-personality, but his wife reminded him that it had led to overaggressive behaviors and decisions being imposed before all the facts were available. She knew this one well and was happy to let him know how this sub-personality disserved their relationship.

If you want to delve further into this, do the following visualization:

- Imagine yourself at a young age, standing in front of the house or apartment you lived in at that age. Visualize the surrounding trees, shrubs, and other buildings. Smell the air around you. Is it familiar?

- Now, walk toward the front door. Notice its color, its handle, and what material it's made of. Slowly open the door and step inside.

- Visualize the interior of the entranceway. Notice the floor, ceiling, and decorations. Are there any familiar smells or sounds?

- Walk toward the kitchen, noticing the details of the environment as you proceed. At the table is one of your parents. Walk to him or her, sit down, and say hello. Listen for a response. What is your parent saying? What do you need your parent to say to you?

- Drift out of your own body and observe the scene below. See yourself as a child, and see your parent there with you. Can you feel the energy of the scene?

- Next, drift into your parent's body. How does it feel? What does your parent need from you, the child there? What does your parent need for you to say?

- Drift out of your parent's body and reenter yours. Say anything else you need to say to your parent. Say good-bye, knowing that you can visit your parent anytime you need to. Walk out of the room and toward the front door. As you open the front door, you become yourself at your current age.

- Slowly open your eyes and come back to the present.

This exercise allows you to better understand your parents, essentially by putting yourself in their shoes. It also allows you to say and do things that you wish you could say, if your parents are living, or could have said, if they have passed. For some of you this may be a sad process, and for some, rather joyous. Each time you repeat this process, something new may occur. I encourage you to use this over and over, especially if you have unresolved parental issues or issues with your own children. In the latter case, look for you in your parent, and look for your child in yourself.

Sub-personality Trait Analysis
(Five Minutes per Personality)

You can further analyze your sub-personalities by evaluating their good and bad sides. Pick one of the sub-personalities you want to understand better. On a separate paper, write its name on the top, draw a picture of it, and list its desirable and undesirable traits around it.

This exercise will help you to understand the good and bad aspects of each personality. I encourage you to do this over and over with each of your predominant sub-personalities. In the ones you consider good, see if you can find ways in which they limit you. In the bad ones, see if you can't find out how they serve you. For example, some of our angry, aggressive sub-personalities provide a way for us to protect ourselves.

The Shadow Personalities

Because our dark characters are so prevalent and because physicians want to be "Glenda, the Good Witch," not the "Wicked Witch of the West," we really work hard at suppressing the dark parts of ourselves.*

Do you want to be good or do you want to be whole?

— Carl Jung, PhD

Carl Jung used the term Shadow to name the parts of ourselves that we do not want to see. The Shadow can be said to be another self, a self that we don't like and therefore have disowned, or a place wherein our darkest secrets and self-loathing reside. This could be our inner Zorro, in response to a Zorro mother. Our Shadow self is composed of sub-personalities from our lower unconscious.

There is both good and evil in the world, but the line separating them runs not between nations or institutions or groups or even individuals; the line that separates good and evil runs through the core of each nation, each institution, each group, and most tellingly, through the core of each human being, through each one of us.

— *The Spirituality of Imperfection* by Kurtz and Keycham

Understanding that each of us carries a Shadow that is both our own and the collective Shadow of existence will help us own our part in what is destructive personally and globally. By healing our inner landscape, we walk with integrity and compassion in relation to others.

The most important misconception about the Shadow side of existence is that it is all negative, bad, wrong, evil, and to be ignored and avoided at all costs. One only need look at religious wars to know that focusing only on the good does not work. Most religions are based on the concept of loving others; yet the nature of humans within these concepts allows us to kill each other to defend our religion. Focusing on being good and avoiding evil without healing our dark side is often what keeps us locked in our own negative reactions and feelings of hatred and mistrust.

The Shadow sub-personalities demand our attention, not because we are evil, or even that evil is stronger than good, but because buried underneath what we loath and disown, lie our creativity and energy. Once we can accept them, then we can work with them. Until we accept these parts of ourselves, we are just stuck.

---

*I want to thank my friend and co-teacher, Nita Gage, for teaching me about this and helping with this section of the chapter.

Trying to ignore and avoid what we don't like about ourselves, what we believe is unacceptable, unfortunately also hides our passion and purpose. To get to our passion and purpose we must be willing to shine the lights on Shadow parts of ourselves.

If we try to be good and not admit when we are angry, the anger will leak out in ways beyond our control, and we will remain stuck in the anger. By acknowledging anger, we are able to make conscious choices about how and when we express that anger.

Experiencing our so-called negative emotions is a necessary pathway to healing. Such emotions as anger, sadness, and fear are stepping-stones through our healing process if we do not ignore and stuff them deeply into the recesses of our Shadow.

For some people, it is joy and happiness that is in their Shadow. Somewhere they learned that it is not safe for them to be happy; perhaps they were around a depressed parent for whom the child's happiness was deemed unwelcome. These people may live with chronic depression, and doing Shadow work will assist in opening up the pathways of joy.

For all, Shadow work will unleash creativity and passion for life. The Shadow is far more liberating and much less disturbing than any of us can imagine.

The Shadow is the part of us that we have disowned and avoided because we are afraid to address it; yet it is still "us"! The Shadow holds many of our fears, such as being less than perfect, of opening up and being vulnerable, and of being seen for who we really are.

Some examples of Shadow thinking:

"I must be good to get what I want." This statement makes the assumption that we will be rewarded for good behavior; yet many of us know that this is not universally true. Interestingly if we don't get what we want, we usually get rather upset.

"All I ever do is give; why don't you love me?" This is also chock-full of resentment and manipulation. Many parents use this one with their children to guilt them into doing what the parents want. It is also a good way to play the martyr.

"Adults are not supposed to have fun." This is a societal repression of joy, passion, and creative energy.

"If I just meditate and eat organically this will all go away." This is Spiritual Bypass. This often serves as a way of avoiding what is really going on in your life by substituting good behaviors without ever dealing with the real issues. It doesn't work. As Ram Dass, the spiritual teacher and philosopher, has said, "When you think that you have reached enlightenment, spend a week with your parents."

Why bother looking at this part of ourselves? Much of our creativity and creative energy comes from the mixing of our Shadow and non-Shadow sub-personalities. By addressing the Shadow, one can unlock this creativity and unblock previously non-addressed issues.

Many great works of art and literature arise from an experience with the Shadow. Artists do their best work after bouts of depression, great personal loss, or even psychosis. Our creativity lies deep within the Shadow and we have the opportunity to reach it.

Humans carry the Shadow individually and collectively. By owning that part of ourselves, we transform more than ourselves, and can begin to truly connect with others. The dysfunctional part about our efforts to hide the Shadow is that they don't work. Everyone else sees it anyway. As physicians, getting in touch with our flaws makes us more realistic and sympathetic toward our patients. The conscious wounded healer is an effective healer.

What happens when we keep the Shadow hidden? It erodes our energy, creativity, and passions.

There are many tried-and-true ways to manage the process of diving into your Shadow self. Examples include the following:

- Twelve-step programs such as A.A.
- Psychotherapy, whether one on one or in a group setting
- In conscious relationship — working with your spouse in healthy ways to explore your respective personalities
- Sweat lodges — the Native American tradition of being with a guided group in a dark tent-like lodge, heated with hot rocks
- Vision quest — the tradition of going on a spiritual journey
- Dance work — movement-related therapies that allow exploration of suppressed sides of your personality
- Transformational workshops and experiences
- Humor — Pokes fun at our dark side, therefore exposing it and allowing us to manage it better
- Artwork — Expressing what may otherwise remain suppressed

The Shadows of the Healer

Our most cherished and useful personality traits have a dark side when taken to extreme. For example, cleanliness and neatness are generally admirable traits, and obsessive-compulsive behavior is pathological and disruptive. Where do you stand in the following traits?

Intelligent/Talented Being intelligent is certainly a desirable trait; however, when intelligence is placed above all else, you lose touch with emotions and the wishes of others. This is known as being "stuck above the neck" with no access to your heart. Have you ever tried to explain to your child, your spouse, or a friend something that comes naturally to you and found yourself mad at that person because he or she seemed stupid? When you don't see intelligence as a gift, you see everyone else as stupid. This is arrogant and judgmental.

Caring Even caring can be taken too far, which enters the realm of overcare or worry. This is not effective or healthy. Staying up worrying about someone else doesn't help that person or you. In medicine, what keeps us awake at night worrying about a patient is fear that we didn't do enough or aren't good enough to take care of someone else. As parents, overcare is a way of manipulating. When we overprotect our children, it is often related to our own fears, not reality. We control through overcare.

Sensitive Being overly sensitive is another way of controlling and avoiding things we don't want to deal with. In essence we use sensitivity as an excuse. This allows us to avoid difficult situations and people, and even helps us avoid making changes in our lives. Many of us would rather sit tight and suffer than make change.

High Integrity On the surface this is an admirable trait; however, when you judge others based on your standard of integrity, this may not be appropriate. It also leads to inflexibility.

Focused Being focused is another trait that is admirable when used in balance. When taken to the point of hyper-focus, we can miss the big picture, allow obsessive tendencies to take over, and become inaccessible and inflexible.

Good Boys and Girls Physicians have an extreme need to be seen as good. This means that they will suppress or hide any thoughts or behaviors that may be perceived as bad. This need is often based in early childhood. If our parents had high expectations (perfectionists) of us, we want them to see how well behaved and talented we are. We therefore learn not only to do good things but also to make sure that they are seen. This way of being is linked to our success and hard to give up, but it is often inauthentic. How many negative thoughts have you suppressed? How many chances have you not taken based on how others might perceive the choice?

This leaves us unsatisfied, perfectionistic, invulnerable, socially isolated, approval seeking, and needing a lot of external validation. It enhances judgmental, competitive, and type-A behaviors. This is not a good place to be, but far too common for physicians.

Objective Taken to extreme, remaining objective is our old protector, also known as emotional dissociation.

Bravery We all like to ride our white horses into battle, especially if someone is watching. Bravery can become very addictive. We end up seeking adrenaline highs, even when they are not real. This creates the false hero. By doing this, our own imperfections will not be seen.

Dark Art
(Twenty-Minute Exercise)

This can be fun and create great insight if you don't allow your fear or rebellion-based sub-personalities to prevent you from doing this. If you have an explorer, playful, or scientist sub-personality, use it to get you motivated.

Do a collage or drawing of your dark side. If you choose to collage, which I recommend, find some old magazines. Take a few minutes with your eyes closed and think about some of the Shadow parts of your personality. Thumb through the magazines and tear out whichever pictures jump out at you. Do not think too much about this. Glue the pictures to a piece of paper. Don't engage your cortex too much. See what you've made and what it says to you. Post it in your house and see if it "speaks" to you over the next few days. Ask you family or friends what they see in it.

You're Never Alone with Multiple Sub-personalities
(Ten-Minute Exercise)

To better understand your sub-personalities and how they arose, sometimes it's useful to spend time with them, especially for with those with which you struggle.

Find a comfortable position. Close your eyes. Pretend that you are walking along a path in a large park. You come upon a broad set of stairs leading downward. You decide to descend the stairs.

As you walk, you see beautiful foliage around you. You smell the plants and fresh air. There may even be some flowers. As you come to the bottom of the stairs, your feet are in soft, cool grass. Ahead of you is a bench. You walk up to it and sit down.

You take some deep breaths and smell the air, the foliage, and the sun on you. As you look around, you see your sub-personalities milling about. Go up to one and say hello. Notice what he or she is wearing.

Ask your sub-personality its name. How old is he or she? Why is that personality there? What happens when that personality is in control?

Invite him or her for a walk. Proceed together up an incline. Take notice of the ground surface. Also, see if the sub-personality changes as you walk up the hill. Stop for a moment and take notice of any changes.

Continue your uphill walk, stopping now and then to observe your sub-personality.

Together, you reach a crest. Look around to see where you are. Observe your sub-personality's clothing, way of standing, and facial expression.

Ask your sub-personality any question you would like an answer to. It could be about the personality or any issue that you are managing.

When you are ready, open your eyes. If you want to write down any intuitive hits or new understandings, take a moment to do so on a sheet of paper or journal.

This process can be used over and over with each sub-personality. It will help you to gain insights into how they serve you and how you can serve them. Do this with your suppressed impulsive self and see how you can serve it. Avoid the midlife crisis!

Make some notes about what you learned in this imagery.

Taking Back the Controls
(Ten-Minute Exercise)

When Duke Ellington was refused a room in the hotel he was to play at, the next day he said, "I merely took the energy it takes to pout and wrote some blues ." He took the angry, dark Duke and made it into the creative Duke. This is truly the power to use dark energy to its fullest.

It is not unusual for a dominant sub-personality to take control of our lives. We often allow this, especially if it feels safe. For example, if it's easier to act the role of doctor and identify completely with that role in order to function, we can do that for long periods. At times, this may seem very functional (for example, when you're working long hours); however, by giving one of your actors the lead role for too long, that actor becomes a bit full of itself. Simultaneously, other actors are being ignored, such as your playful self, your creative self, your academic self, or others. Think of this as a form of delayed gratification. At some point this breaks down, so that you essentially have you an actors' strike. What you need is a good director to use the actors to their best abilities and keep balance among them.

In her book *Soul Play: Turning Your Daily Dramas into Divine Comedies*, Vivian King uses the concept of your sub-personalities as actors in your life play.[3] You are the director and God is the playwright. I want to use this model to help you to regain control.

If your life is a play and your sub-personalities are the actors, who is the director? The last exercise helped show that you are not your emotions, you are not your left leg, and you are not the doctor. So, who are you?

Let's get closer to that person or soul. Since the heart is the seat of the soul, let's go to that seat.

Find a comfortable position and breathe deeply and slowly through the area around your heart.

Take a moment to think of someone you love. Spend a few moments with that person in your mind and heart.

Think of the outside of a theater building. It can be as simple or ornate as you like. Bring your mind and heart to the theater.

Walk through its doors and into the atrium. Look around and notice the details.

Enter the portal to the main auditorium. Walk toward the stage. Notice some steps leading you onto the stage, and climb them.

Somewhere behind the curtains is your chair. Look for it. Once you've found it, study it for a moment. Is it simple, ornate, soft, or bench-like? Is it well worn or brand new? Has it been used lately?

Bring it to the front of the stage and down the steps. Seat yourself in it, facing the stage. Now call out your sub-personalities onto the stage. Identify and greet each one. Thank them for agreeing to be in your play.

You are now ready to be the director of your own play!

Assessing Your Cast of Characters

As you observe your cast lined up onstage, you may notice that some are true stars, others are bit players, and some with star qualities may be young and unsure of their roles.

Take a moment to look at each cast member and rate him or her as potential star or bit player. See whether they need coaching work or just your support and acknowledgement in their roles.

Managing the Troublemakers
(Ten-Minute Exercise)

Are any of your cast members abusive to other cast members? Do any of them tend to upstage others? Let's find out what they need from us in order to manage them with respect and love.

Find a comfortable position. Close your eyes. Pretend that you are walking along a path in a large park. You come upon a broad set of stairs leading downward. You decide to descend the stairs.

As you walk, you see beautiful foliage around you. You smell the plants and fresh air. There may even be some flowers. As you come to the bottom of the stairs, your feet are in soft, cool grass. Ahead of you is a bench. You walk up to it and sit down.

You take some deep breaths and smell the air and the foliage, and feel the sun on you.

Look for the sub-personality that is troublesome. Go up to one and say hello. Notice his or her clothes and stance. Is this personality proud? Shy? Gloating? Embarrassed?

Go to your heart and try to express love for that personality. Let that personality know you care and appreciate having him or her onboard.

Invite the personality for a walk. Proceed together up an incline. Take notice of the ground surface. Notice if the sub-personality changes as you walk up the hill. Stop for a moment and take notice of any changes in the sub-personality or the surroundings.

Continue your uphill walk, stopping now and then to observe your sub-personality.

Together, you reach a crest. Look around to see your surroundings. Observe your sub-personality's stance, facial expression, and clothing.

Now ask this cast member what needs to be done to help him or her excel. Listen for an answer. If there is not one, ask how you can support his or her growth.

If this sub-personality acts in a manner that you're no longer willing to tolerate, ask this personality what will stop this behavior.

When you are ready, open your eyes. If you want to write down any intuitive insights or new understandings, take a moment to do so on a piece of paper or journal.

Accessing the Playwright
(Ten-Minute Exercise)

Who has written the story that you are directing. This role may be that of God, the soul, the universe, the transpersonal self, or another manner of thinking that is comfortable and desirable for you.

When you feel stuck as the director, it is sometimes helpful to access the playwright.

Sit comfortably in your director's chair. Look around at the theater that has been given to you. Appreciate and study it for a while.

Now look at your cast of sub-personalities; appreciate and honor their attributes.

Let's take a few minutes and write a letter to the playwright. If you need help in directing, ask your higher power. If you do not, just thank your playwright for the opportunity to direct this play.

If in this process you receive information from your playwright and feel unsure, ask yourself the following:

1. Does this information ring true?
2. Is it loving and compassionate?
3. Does it empower others and me?

If the answers are yes, then this is true information.

Self-Identification or Dis-identification

We are dominated by everything with which we become identified. We can dominate everything from which we dis-identify.

— Roberto Assagioli, MD, 1965

Damn it, Jim, I'm a doctor.

— Dr. Leonard McCoy, United Starship Enterprise

We tend to define ourselves in very limited terms. This places us in a one-dimensional box. If your total identity is that of a doctor, then you're not a lover, a musician, a ball player, or a dancer. You limit your possible thought processes and creativity. It is as if you lock yourself into, or identify too closely with, one of your sub-personalities. The extreme example of this is a person with multiple personalities. This person completely identifies or associates with each inner personality, to the point where each is distinct from the others.

Wouldn't it be great to have access to all of your behavioral styles and thought processes simultaneously and to use those attributes when you needed them! This is the role of dis-identifying. Dis-identifying is to become a calm observer of your reactions and behaviors while still in a given situation. It allows you to pick and choose which "you" you want to be at any given moment. In the structure of consciousness, this is reaching the center.

Let's look at the concept of "you." What is the irreducible "you"? If you lose your right hand, are you still you? If you have a stroke and can't speak, are you still you? If you change careers, are you still you?

There are times when we overidentify with our emotions, for example, "I am angry" or "I am afraid." Are you angry, or are you experiencing anger?

If it truly were you, there would be no way out of it; however, to look at the emotion as a transient experience helps you to calm the emotion and assess what is causing you to feel anger (not be anger). Although this may seem like a subtle difference, with enough experience this can begin to shift you into a calmer, more objective, state of being. This can be described as self-identification, or identifying with your true self rather than the job or emotion of the moment.

I have anger. I am not the anger.

I Am Myself
(Five-Minute Exercise)

Become the impartial witness; come to the center to see your self-worth.
Do the following visualization anytime you feel overly emotionally involved and wish to become more objective.

The body:

1. Sit in a comfortable position.
2. Breath in and out deeply and slowly.
3. Become aware of the feeling of breath moving in and out.
4. Focus on your feet; feel them in your shoes, socks, or the floor beneath them. Are they tired? Are they sore?
5. Focus on your leg muscles. How do they feel? Are they relaxed?
6. Move your focus up throughout your body. Check in with each area.
7. Remind yourself that if you lost your foot, you would still be you.
8. Say to yourself, "I have a body, but I am not my body."

Your feelings:

1. Focus now on your feelings.
2. What feeling or emotion do you have now?
3. What feelings have you had recently? Anger? Jealousy? Love?
4. Do not judge them as right or wrong. Just observe them.
5. Remember what each feels like, look at it objectively, and then let it go.
6. Say to yourself, "I have feelings, but I am not my feelings."

Your desires:

1. Next focus on what you want.
2. Observe each one without judgment and let it go.
3. Say to yourself, "I have desires, but I am not my desires."

Your thoughts:

1. Calmly observe thoughts as they enter your consciousness.
2. After you've observed one, imagine that you are placing it a box. This will allow you to get it later if you need it. Let go and move on to the next thought. Remember, if you say to yourself, "Where is my next thought?" that too is a thought.
3. Say to yourself, "I have thoughts, but I am not my thoughts."

Yourself:

1. Who has been the observer in all of the above exercises? It is your "self"?
2. Repeat to yourself, "I am the self, the center of pure consciousness."

> *The marriage between the higher self and self-worth is wisdom. My wisdom then allows me to use my parts in any way I want*

> — Virginia Satir, 1988

Yours, Mine, and Ours: The Sub-personalities in Relationship

If each of us has ten sub-personalities, then each couple can have twenty sub-personalities with a hundred possible combinations of these at any given time. In this model, a family of four would have up to eighty different personalities living together under one roof. The possible combinations of personalities in a given room is extraordinary. It's amazing we get along at all!

How can we use this understanding to enhance our relationships? First, it's important to note that many of your partner's sub-personalities are attractive or complementary to many of yours; otherwise you probably would not be together.

When you have some quiet time, go through each other's sub-personalities, not to judge them, but to acknowledge and accept them. This can be a very useful way of understanding each other's way of being and responding. When you become practiced at this, you can begin to ask for a sub-personality by name: "Honey, I need you to be the Practical One in this decision; I'm a little bit the Mushy One tonight."

You can work together to enhance the role of each other's desired sub-personalities in the relationship by finding out what a desired sub-personality needs to succeed.

This helps you to be a calm observer of difficult moments in your relationship and therefore to manage those moments more clearly and calmly.

CHAPTER 16 **Moving Forward**

This chapter describes an important restructuring process. Give yourself one hour, if not longer, to do the work in this chapter. If you are married, you may wish to read with your spouse the parts of this chapter about your life together.

How would you like your life to be different from how it is today? It may need a major overhaul or just some fine-tuning. It may be that you wouldn't change much about the events of your day, just your attitude. It may be that your plate is too full and you want to hone it down a bit. Whatever your goals are, this chapter will help you create a plan and enhance your goal achievement capacity to higher levels using the concepts of psychosynthesis, emotional shifting, and a new tool, appreciative inquiry.

Create Your Mission Statement

A mission statement is your description of your life purpose, on a global level. What is it that you wish to accomplish in this life? Do you want to create a new generation of medical leaders? Do you want to be a loving parent? Do you want to serve as many people as you can?

It is important to know your life purpose as you create your goals to move forward. I encourage you to write a two to three sentence mission statement. For example, my mission statement is as follows:

> *I will help physicians to gain a sense of clarity and emotional intelligence in order to recreate their lives in a way that serves them and their patients, with the long-term goal of recreating our system of medicine into a more humane, caring, and effective system. I will be a loving father, husband, and friend.*

As you decide where you want your life to go, what tasks to take on, what to keep on the plate, and what to let go of, measure these decisions against your mission statement. If they fit, go for it. If they don't distract you from your mission, that may be okay too. If they distract you from your mission, don't do go through with them.

Create Your Vision Statement

The mission statement is broad reaching and large in nature. It does not describe how you will reach your goals. That is the vision statement. The vision statement is an overview of your plan to accomplish the mission statement. Here is an example:

I will accomplish my mission in the following ways:

1. *Deliver workshops and seminars to aid physicians and their families.*
2. *Create books, CDs, and videos to teach physicians.*
3. *Consult with health systems toward helping their physicians thrive.*
4. *Train medical school and residency faculty to teach appropriate tools to their students and residents.*
5. *Train other teachers to work in the private sectors of medicine to achieve the mission faster and more globally.*
6. *Work with and help establish international societies focusing on physician well-being.*
7. *Carve out and hold sacred time with my family and friends and maintain good boundaries to protect this time.*
8. *Maintain my practices of self-growth in order to accomplish all of the above.*

While this vision statement may feel daunting, write down your plans for today. Keep in mind that these missions and visions may change over time. The only truth I know about the five-year business plan is that it is good for about six months. Mission and vision plans have longer duration but will change over time, more subtly than a business plan.

Why is this process so important, even if it may change? It allows you the standard on which to base all of your upcoming decisions about your life. Without this, you will be floundering around without a paddle.

One word of caution in creating a plan: you are very smart and capable, and this may be a problem. Capable people can do lots of things well, so when they create plans and goals, there are many viable options. They often end up stuck between two or three good options. At some point you will need to choose and just go for it. To do this, use your meditation practice to sit with the options and see which one resonates for you. Don't think too much; use your intuition. Also, use the Freeze-Frame technique to drop into your heart and see if the answer is already there.

Finding Goals
The following will be a series of goals that you may wish to achieve in moving forward. Work with each one and see how it fits within your mission and vision statements.

Sub-personality Goals
One goal may be to support one of your sub-personalities that has not had a chance to "flex its muscles" for a while. My particular favorite is the rebellious one, but you can choose the one you wish to work with.

The first step is to identify that sub-personality, describe its personality characteristics, where it came from, and maybe even journey with it as we did in the preceding chapter, to see what it needs.

The second step is to find ways to support that sub-personality.

1. Close your eyes and begin taking deep breaths.
2. See yourself in the role of that sub-personality and ask what you can do to allow its expression.
3. Make a list of ways to support this sub-personality.
4. Keep this list to be included in your action plan.

Changing a Personal Issue

Is there a personal issue that you want to work on? More exercise, losing weight, or maybe spending more time with family?

How is this apparent in your life? Do you feel uncomfortable, or do you have stress in your relationships? What would happen, moving forward, if you didn't change this issue?

The first step in moving this forward is to lay out what you would need to do to resolve the issue, then assess what you would have to give up to resolve the issue. With this in mind, you can then decide if it is worth pursuing.

Many of us get stuck thinking we should do this, that, or the other because it's what we are supposed to do. For example, we get frustrated with having gained ten pounds, but rather than do something about it, we live with it in frustration. By laying out what you would need to do to resolve the problem, you can choose whether to do it or not. Then you are not the victim anymore; you are in charge of the choice.

Lastly, list the positive and negative outcomes of resolving this issue. It is critical to identify both the positive and negative issues in making a life change so that you have full awareness going into the change. Some of the negatives may include your own secondary gain. For instance, if being overweight protects you from having to do too much, this is a secondary gain.

If you decide to move this forward, add it to the list for your action plan. If you decide not to move it forward, you have shifted your attitude about the issue, so let it go.

Planning for the Future

Let's look at long-term goals. Where would you like to be in the next five and ten years; for example, working less or downsizing your life (smaller home, simpler life). An anesthesiologist friend of mine decided he want to be in farming and created a five-year plan to wean into this new life. It's your dream, you decide.

Then consider what you would need to do to get to that place. What would it take and is it worth the effort? Is it just an unrealistic goal or is it worth manifesting? What would you have to give up to get there? By looking at all these issues you can then decide if this is truly where you wish to go.

If it is the goal, what are you doing now that will slow or prevent you from getting there? It is important to realize that sometimes we obstruct our own missions. It is also useful to note that sometimes the wanting is more fun than the getting. If you are one of those who enjoys the wanting, that's fine; just be aware of this.

Acknowledging Relationship Goals
Some goals may be in the interpersonal-relationship category. For instance maybe something important has been left unsaid, such as an apology or expression of love for the other person. To put this in context, if you had one month to live, what would you want to say to friends and family? This is an important question, so take time in considering it. Write this on your list of goals.

Achieving a Dream
The ultimate goals may come from the following question: If you had one year to live, what would you choose to do? I encourage you to make a list and discuss this with your loved ones. After being diagnosed with metastatic breast cancer, a friend of mine decided to spend the last year of her life visiting friends and family. She also allowed her friends and family to take care of her, cook for her, and do the housekeeping. A year later I asked her husband what that was like for them. He said it had been the best year of their life. Maybe it's time we start living as if we were dying, because we are. I also believe that learning how to be ready to die teaches us how to live.

Developing the Will to Move Forward
Now that you have established potential goals, let's begin the process of developing your will to achieve your goals and overcome any fears you may have.

Your will is the driving force that moves you out of stagnation, yet many of us fear our will and are adverse to using power to move things in a desired direction.

Unfortunately we have all seen power abused and may have done so ourselves. This is often the case when our will is out of balance with our intention. How can we find a way to use power and will to do good work when needed?

Assagioli described four types of will:

1. Strong will — Gets things moving quickly and often dramatically
2. Skillful will — Exhibits great cunning and ability to plan, imagine, and intuit
3. Good will — Expresses compassion and love
4. Transpersonal will — Serves humankind and the planet[1]

If I had a Volkswagen and wanted to move it two blocks away, my strong will would push it; my skillful will would get in, start the engine, and drive it; my good will would pick up someone on the way and give them a lift; and my transpersonal will might decide not to drive it at all because I would pollute the air.

Each of these types of will is extremely useful; however, when out of balance with the others, each can be quite dangerous. For example, strong will without compassion can be overly forceful and abusive, and good will alone can be indecisive, nondirected, and ineffective. Skillful will without caring can be manipulative. Transpersonal will without skill or strength can be ineffective, essentially resulting in good thoughts and wishes without action.

I encourage you to think of willfulness as a tool that can be used to do good in the world; it's not just manipulative or aggressive!

Appreciative Inquiry

Now we are ready to do some planning. With the goals you've established and the mission and vision statements you have written, I want to help you move forward into the next year.

The technique I will show you is called *appreciative inquiry*.[2] It is a technique used in business to move a plan forward, based on the strengths of the past. In theory, most people create plans to fix what is broken. This creates a focus on what is not working as opposed to what is working. As I had described earlier, focusing on the negative increases catecholamines and cortisol, and diminishes cortical function. This creates a feeling of being stuck. Appreciative inquiry helps you focus on what works, makes you feel good about it, lowers catecholamines, and therefore enhances cortical function and creativity. Let's begin.

I encourage you to take a piece of paper or your computer and write the following:

1. Recall a time when you had an exceptional moment in your work interrelationships, a time when you felt as if you were born to do what you do.
   a. Write a description of that time as if you were telling a story.
   b. Who was involved in the success of this moment?
   c. What qualities in others helped make this a success?
   d. Which of your qualities made it work and what sub-personalities were involved?
2. Now look for themes: Did you rely on others? Was the task larger than you believed you could manage? What was your emotional attitude?

Note: You can do this process with others or a working team. It works great. In that situation, each person shares his or her story and looks for common, group themes.

3. Now, close your eyes and imagine that you fall asleep tonight and wake up one year later. Your life is what you want it to be. Write down what your day looks like one year from now. Whom will you see, where will you be, and what will you do?
4. Now make a list of at least five steps you will need to make to get there in the next week, next month, next three months, and the next six months. Make each step manageable and reasonable. This becomes your action plan for moving forward.

Sample Action Plan
As I write this, I am in a state of growth with my programs. I am also celebrating my fiftieth birthday this year, so my action plans will include these things.

This week:

1. Finish this book.
2. Start a rewrite of my medical school and residency curricular materials.
3. Plan my travel for the next three months.
4. Go out to hear some live music.
5. Take the family out for Valentine's Day dinner.

This month:

1. Finish the rewrite of my medical school and residency curriculum.
2. Get this book edited.
3. Find a graphic designer to create the book cover.
4. Schedule summer training sessions for residency faculty.
5. Get Web site content finished.
6. See more live music.
7. Get back on my bike (once the rain stops).
8. Play tennis with my daughter.
9. Get a massage.
10. Plan summer fiftieth birthday travel.

The next three months:

1. Lock in a site for summer training.
2. Create Web linkages with other programs and clients.
3. Schedule attendance for at least two medical meetings as an exhibitor.
4. Get exhibit booth created and produced.
5. Get book published.
6. Schedule fall speaking engagements.
7. Enjoy a great (not just good) bottle of wine.

I used this simple technique in moving from my role as medical director of a research institute to the CEO of Finding Balance, Inc. I created a three-year plan of weaning from one job to the other with great success. With each part of the plan, reflect back to your mission and vision statements to see if you are moving toward them. You want to make sure that your plan keeps you on target.

I encourage you to create your action plan, share it with your family, and leave it posted somewhere in the house or office. The only way to move forward is to take it one step at a time. The plan will help you to do that. Every month, revisit the plan to make changes as needed.

---

*footnote to the cognitive shifting chapter. My son's room is now clean, but the dog still needs a bath. Oh, well – partial success without a lot of yelling

CHAPTER 17 **What Is Balance?**

Balance is being realistic about what you can control and what you can't.

Balance is learning to accept and appreciate your own limitations.

Balance is the willingness and courage to evaluate yourself and make changes when needed.

Balance is remembering to love those people in your life who give you meaning and purpose.

Balance is finding reasons to love even the difficult people in your life.

Balance is learning to love yourself. You may be one of the difficult ones.

Balance is to remember that "they" might be right.

Balance is learning to understand, love, and embrace the part of your personality with which you struggle.

Balance is taking care of yourself first, so that you can take care of your family. Then, coming from a stable and loving home, you can serve your patients.

Balance is listening with your heart.

Balance is taking care of the body you've been given.

Balance is knowing that you will make mistakes, and learning from them.

Balance is being open to new ways of thinking.

Balance is exploring and learning.

Balance is seeing the big picture through love and spirituality.

Balance is service.

Balance is knowing that today is a good day to die; that you have lived fully, lovingly, and without remorse.

Notes

Chapter 2: Are We Happy?

1. E. Frank, McMurray J. E.; Linzer M.; Elon L. ., "Career Satisfaction of U.S. Women Physicians: Results from the Women Physicians' Health Study," *Archives of Internal Medicine* 159 (July 12, 1999): 13.

2. Medstat Group and J. D. Power and Associates survey (1998); http://www.medstat.com/

3. J. E. McMurray et al., "The Work Lives of Women Physicians: Results from the Physician Work-life Study," The SGIM Career Satisfaction Study Group, *Journal of General Internal Medicine* 6 (June 15, 2000): 372–80.

4. L. Nonnemaker, "Women Physicians in Academic Medicine, *New England Journal of Medicine* 342 (2000): 399–405.

5. D. E. Stewart et al., "Women Physicians and Stress," *Journal of Women's Health* 9 (2000): 185–190.

6. Mamta Gautam, "Women in Medicine: Stresses and Solutions," *Western Journal of Medicine* 174 (2001): 37–41.

7. M. A. Miller and R. H. Rahe, "Life Changes Scaling for the 1990s," *Journal of Psychosomatic Research* 43, no. 3 (September 1997): 279–92.

8. R. Goetzel; et al.; The Health Enhancement Research Organization (HERO) Research Committee; "The Relationship Between Modifiable Health Risks and Health Care Expenditures: An Analysis of the Multi-Employer HERO Health Risk and Cost Database." *Journal of Occupational and Environmental Medicine* 40, no. 10 (October 1998): 1–12.

Chapter 4: The Physician Personality

1. Menninger, R., Stress: defining the personal equation , *British Medical Journal* 29, Careers section, (March 2003), p. 326:S107

2. Erica Frank et al., "Experiences of Belittlement and Harassment and Their Correlates among Medical Students in the United States: Longitudinal Survey," *British Medical Journal* (September 6, 2006), BMJ.org doi:10.1136/bmj.38924.722037.7C.

Chapter 5: **Our Health**

1. E. Heim, "Job Stressors and Coping in Health Professions," *Psychotherapy and Psychosomatics* 55 (1991): 90–9.

2. B. B. Arnetz, "White Collar Stress: What Studies of Physicians Can Teach Us," *Psychotherapy and Psychosomatics* 55 (1991): 197–200.

3. Erica Frank, Holly Biola, and Carol A. Burnett, "Mortality Rates and Causes among U.S. Physicians," *American Journal of Preventive Medicine* 19, no. 3 (October 2000): 155–65.

4. C. D. Delnevo, D. J. Abatemarco, and A. R. Gotsch, "Health Behaviors and Health Promotion: Disease Prevention Perceptions of Medical Students," *American Journal of Preventive Medicine* 12 (1996): 38–43.

5. Alan Rozanski, James A. Blumenthal, and Jay Kaplan, "Impact of Psychological Factors on the Pathogenesis of Cardiovascular Disease and Implications for Therapy," *Circulation* 99 (1999): 2192–217.

6. C. Center et al., "Confronting Depression and Suicide in Physicians: A Consensus Statement," *Journal of the American Medical Association* 289 (2003): 3161–166.

7. N. Frasure-Smith, F. Lesperance, and M. Talajic, "Depression and Eighteen-Month Prognosis after Myocardial Infarction," *Circulation* 91 (1995): 999–1005.

8. J. Denoillet and D. L. Brutsaert, "Personality, Disease Severity, and the Risk of Long-Term Cardiac Events in Patients with a Decreased Ejection Fraction after Myocardial Infarction," *Circulation* 97 (1998): 167–173.

9. N. Frasure-Smith et al., "Gender, Depression, and One-Year Prognosis after Myocardial Infarction," *Psychosomatic Medicine* 61 (1999): 26–37.

10. R. Anda et al., "Depressed Affect, Hopelessness, and the Risk of Ischemic Heart Disease in a Cohort of U.S. Adults," *Epidemiology* 4 (1993): 285–94.

11. A. Arooma et al., "Depression and Cardiovascular Diseases," *Acta Psychiatrica Scandinavica* 377(suppl) (1994): 77–82.

12. T. Vogt et al., "Mental Health Status as a Predictor of Morbidity and Mortality: A Fifteen-Year Follow-up of Members of a Health Maintenance Organization," *American Journal of Public Health* 84 (1994): 227–31.

13. S. A. Everson et al., "Hopelessness and Risk of Mortality and Incidence of Myocardial Infarction and Cancer," *Psychosomatic Medicine* 58 (1996): 113–21.

14. J. Barefoot and M. Schroll, "Symptoms of Depression, Acute Myocardial Infarction, and Total Mortality in a Community Sample," *Circulation* 93 (1996): 1976–80.

15. D. E. Ford et al., "Depression Is a Risk Factor for Coronary Artery Disease in Men," *Archives of Internal Medicine* 158 (1998): 1422–26.

16. R. M. Carney et al., "Major Depressive Disorder Predicts Cardiac Events in Patients with Coronary Artery Disease," *Psychosomatic Medicine* 50 (1988): 627–33.

17. D. K. Ahern et al., "Biobehavioral Variables and Mortality or Cardiac Arrest in the Cardiac Arrhythmia Pilot Study (CAPS)," *American Journal of Cardiology* 66 (1990): 59–62.

18. J. C. Barefoot, M. J. Helms, and D. B. Mark, "Depression and Long-Term Mortality Risk in Patients with Coronary Artery Disease," *American Journal of Cardiology* 78 (1996): 613–17.

19. C. Hermann et al., "Diagnosis Groups and Depressed Mood as Predictors of Twenty-two-Month Mortality in Medical Patients," *Psychosomatic Medicine* 60 (1998): 570–77.

20. J. G. Bruhn et al., "Psychological Predictors of Sudden Death in Myocardial Infarction," *Journal of Psychosomatic Research* 18 (1974): 187–91.

21. François Lespérance et al., "Five-Year Risk of Cardiac Mortality in Relation to Initial Severity and One-Year Changes in Depression Symptoms after Myocardial Infarction," *Circulation* Mar 2002; 105: 1049 - 1053

22. D. E. Bush et al., "Even Minimal Symptoms of Depression Increase Mortality Risk after Acute Myocardial Infarction," *American Journal of Cardiology* 88, no. 4 (August 15, 2001;): 337–41.

23. A. A. Ariyo et al., "Depressive Symptoms and Risks of Coronary Heart Disease and Mortality in Elderly Americans," Cardiovascular Health Study Collaborative Research Group, *Circulation* 102, no. 15 (October 10, 2000): 1773–9.

24. C. B. Nemeroff et al., "Elevated Concentrations of CSF Corticotropin

Releasing Factor-like Immunoreactivity in Depressed Patients," *Science* 226 (1984): 1342–4.

25. Judith A. Whitworth, George J. Mangos, and John J. Kelly, "Cushing, Cortisol, and Cardiovascular Disease," *Hypertension* 36 (2000): 912.

26. Robert Fraser et al., "Cortisol Effects on Body Mass, Blood Pressure, and Cholesterol in the General Population," *Hypertension* 33 (1999): 1364–8.

27. Alistair I. Fyfe et al., "Association between Serum Amyloid A Proteins and Coronary Artery Disease: Evidence from Two Distinct Arteriosclerotic Processes," *Circulation* 96 (1997): 2914–9.

28. R. C. Veith, et al., "Sympathetic Nervous System Activity in Major Depression: Basal and Desipramine-Induced Alterations in Plasma Norepinephrine Kinetics," *Archives of General Psychiatry* 51, no. 5 (May 1994): 411–22.

29. D. L. Musselman et al., "Exaggerated Platelet Reactivity in Major Depression," *American Journal of Psychiatry* 153 (1996):1313–7.

30. F. Laghrissi-Thode et al., "Elevated Platelet Factor 4 and Beta-Thromboglobulin Plasma Levels in Depressed Patients with Ischemic Heart Disease," *Biological Psychiatry* 42 (1997): 290–5.

31. Roland von Känel et al., "Effects of Psychological Stress and Psychiatric Disorders on Blood Coagulation and Fibrinolysis: A Biobehavioral Pathway to Coronary Artery Disease?" *Psychosomatic Medicine* 63 (2001): 531–44.

32. Task Force of the European Society of Cardiology and the North American Society for Pacing and Electrophysiology, *Circulation* 93 (1996): 1043–65.

33. Robert M. Carney et al., "Depression, Heart Rate Variability, and Acute Myocardial Infarction," *Circulation* 104 (2001): 2024.

34. M. Friedman and R. H. Rosenman, "Association of Specific Overt Behavior Pattern with Blood and Cardiovascular Findings: Blood Cholesterol Level, Blood Clotting Time, Incidence of Arcus Senilis, and Clinical Coronary Artery Disease," *Journal of the American Medical Association* 169 (1959): 1286–96.

35. J. Barefoot, W. G. Dahlstrom, R. B. Williams, "Hostility, CHD Incidence, and Total Mortality: A Twenty-five-Year Follow-up Study of 255 Physicians," *Psychosomatic Medicine* 45 (1983): 59–63.

36. I. Kawachi et al., "Decreased Heart Rate Variability in Men with Phobic Anxiety (Data from the Normative Aging Study)," *American Journal of Cardiology* 75 (1995): 882–5.

37. L. F. Berkman and S. L. Syme, "Social Networks, Host Resistance, and Mortality: A Nine-Year Follow-up Study of Alameda County Residents," *American Journal of Epidemiology* 109 (1979): 186–204.

38. K. Orth-Gomer, A. Rosengren, and L. Wilhelmsen, "Lack of Social Support and Incidence of Coronary Heart Disease in Middle-Aged Swedish Men," *Psychosomatic Medicine* 55 (1993): 37–43.

39. J. S. House, C. Robbins, and H. L. Metzner, "The Association of Social Relationships and Activities with Mortality: Prospective Evidence from the Tecumseh Community Health Study," *American Journal of Epidemiology* 116 (1982): 123–40.

40. D. Reed et al., "Social Networks and Coronary Heart Disease among Japanese Men in Hawaii," *American Journal of Epidemiology* 117 (1983): 384–96.

41. L. Welin et al., "Prospective Study of Social Influences on Mortality: The Study of Men Born in 1913 and 1923," *Lancet* 2 (1985): 915–8.

42. V. J. Schoenbach et al., "Social Ties and Mortality in Evans County, Georgia," *American Journal of Epidemiology* 123 (1986): 577–91.

43. K. Orth-Gomer and J. V. Johnson, "Social Network Interaction and Mortality: A Six-Year Follow-up Study of a Random Sample of the Swedish Population," *Journal of Chronic Disease* 40 (1987): 949–57.

44. G. A. Kaplan et al., "Social Connections and Mortality from All Causes and from Cardiovascular Disease: Prospective Evidence from Eastern Finland," *American Journal of Epidemiology* 128 (1988): 370–80.

45. T. Vogt et al., "Social Networks as Predictors of Ischemic Heart Disease, Cancer, Stroke and Hypertension: Incidence, Survival, and Mortality," *Journal of Clinical Epidemiology* 45 (1992): 659–66.

46. G. A. Kaplan et al., "Social Functioning and Overall Mortality: Prospective Evidence from the Kuopio Ischemic Heart Disease Risk Factor Study," *Epidemiology* 5 (1994): 495–500.

47. T. E. Seeman et al., "Social Network Ties and Morality among the Elderly in the Alameda County Study. *American Journal of Epidemiology* 126 (1987): 714–23.

48. C. B. Thomas and K. R. Duszynski, "Closeness to Parents and the Family Constellation in a Prospective Study of Five Disease States: Suicide, Mental Illness, Malignant Tumor, Hypertension and Coronary Artery Disease," *Johns Hopkins Medical Journal* 134 (1974): 251.

Chapter 6: **Stress and Burnout**

1. C. D. Delnevo, D. J. Abatemarco, et al., "Health Behaviors and Health Promotion/Disease Prevention Perceptions of Medical Students," *American Journal of Preventive Medicine* 12, no. 1 (1996): 38–43.

2. J. Firth-Cozens, "The Psychological Problems of Doctors," in J. Firth-Cozens and R. Payne, eds., *Stress in Health Professionals: Psychological and Organizational Causes and Interventions* (London: Wiley, 1999).

3. E. Heim, "Job Stressors and Coping in Health Professions," *Psychotherapy and Psychosomatics* 55 (1991): 90–9.

Chapter 8: **What Makes a Happy Doc Happy?**

1. Shanaree Brown and Richard B. Gunderman, "Viewpoint: Enhancing the Professional Fulfillment of Physicians," *Academic Medicine* 81, no. 6 (June 2006): 577–82.

2. E. Frank et al., "Career Satisfaction of U.S. Women Physicians: Results from the Women Physicians' Health Study," *Archives of Internal Medicine* 159, no. 13 (July 12, 1999) 13.

3. Rein Lepnurm et al., "Factors Explaining Career Satisfaction among Psychiatrists and Surgeons in Canada," *Canadian Journal of Psychiatry, 51* (March 2006) 243-255.

4. M. Linzer et al., "Physician Job Stress: Results from the Physician Work-Life Survey," *Stress and Health* 18 (2002): 37–42.

5. F. Herzberg, "One More Time: How Do You Motivate Employees?" *Harvard Business Review* 81 (2003): 87–96.

6. J. Haas et al., "Is the Professional Satisfaction of General Internists Associated with Patient Satisfaction?" *Journal of General Internal Medicine* 15 (2000): 122–8.

7. D. Grembowski et al., "Managed Care, Physician Job Satisfaction, and the Quality of Primary Care," *Journal of General Internal Medicine* 20 (2005): 271–7.

8. J. Sundquist and S. Johansson, "High Demand, Low Control, and Impaired General Health: Working Conditions in a Sample of Swedish General Practitioners," *Scandinavian Journal of Public Health* 28 (2000): 123–31.

9. B. Beasley, D. Kern, and K. Kolodner, "Job Turnover and Its Correlates among Residency Program Directors in Internal Medicine," Academic Medicine 76 (2001): 1127–35.

10. S. Buchbinder et al., "Primary Care Physician Job Satisfaction and Turnover," *American Journal of Managed Care* 7 (2001): 702–13.

11. S. Buchbinder et al., "Estimates of Costs of Primary Care Physician Turnover," *American Journal of Managed Care* 5 (1999): 1431–38.

12. Shelley E. Taylor et al., "Biobehavioral Responses to Stress in Females: Tend-and-Befriend, Not Fight-or-Flight," *Psychological Review* 107, no. 3 (July 2000): 411–29.

Chapter 10: A Cognitive Approach to Perspective Shifting

1. David Burns, *The Feeling Good Handbook* (New York: Plume, 1990).

2. Albert Ellis, *A New Guide to Rational Living* (Los Angeles: Wilshire Book Company, 1961).

Chapter 11: Emotional Shifting and Emotional Intelligence

1. D. Childre and H. Martin, *The HeartMath Solution* (San Francisco: HarperSanFrancisco, 1999).

2. B. Barrios-Choplin, "Restructuring Employees' Interpretive Styles to Reduce Tension and Burnout: One Company's Experience," working paper (1997) on-line at HeartMath.org.

3. B. Barrios-Choplin, R. McCraty, and B. Cryer, "An Inner Quality Approach to Reducing Stress and Improving Physical and Emotional Well-being at Work," *Stress Medicine* 13 (1997): 193–201.

4. R. McCraty et al., "The impact of a New Emotional Self-Management Program on Stress, Emotions, Heart Rate Variability, DHEA, and Cortisol," *Integrative Physiological and Behavioral Science* 33, no. 2 (1998): 151.

5. D. Rozman et al., "A Pilot Intervention Program which Reduces Psychological Symptomatology in Individuals with Human Immunodeficiency Virus," *Complementary Therapies in Medicine* 4 (1996): 226.

6. R. McCraty et al., "The Effects of Emotions on Short-Term Heart Rate Variability using Power Spectrum Analysis," *American Journal of Cardiology* 76 (1995): 1089.

7. W. Tiller, R. McCraty, and M. Atkinson, "Cardiac Coherence: A New, Noninvasive Measure of Autonomic Nervous System Order," *Alternative Therapies in Health and Medicine* 2, no. 1 (1996): 52.

8. G. Rein, M. Atkinson, and R. McCraty, "The Physiological and Psychological Effects of Compassion and Anger," *Journal of Advancement in Medicine* 8, no. 2 (1995): 87.

9. F. Luskin et al., "Controlled Pilot of Stress Management Training of Elderly Patients with Congestive Heart Failure," *Preventive* Cardiology 2002;5(4):168-172, 176.

10. Rollin McCraty et al., "Impact of the HeartMath Self-Management Skills Program on Physiological and Psychological Stress in Police Officers," HeartMath Research Center, publication no. 99-075. (Boulder Creek: Institute of HeartMath, 1999).

11. Vaishnav S, Stevenson R, Marchant B, Lagi K, Ranjadayalan K, Timmis AD. "Relation between Heart Rate Variability Early after Acute Myocardial Infarction and Long-term Mortality." American Journal of Cardiology 73 (1994): 653–7.

12. Y. Khaykin, et al., "Autonomic Correlates of Antidepressant Treatment using Heart Rate Variability Analysis," *Canadian Journal of Psychiatry* 43 (1998): 183–6.

13. J. A. Blumenthal, et al., "Usefulness of Psychosocial Treatment of Mental Stress-Induced Myocardial Ischemia in Men," *American Journal of Cardiology* 89, no. 2 (January 15,2002): 164–8.

14. Luciano Bernardi et al., "Heart Rate Variability Enhanced by Prayer and Mantra Recitation," British Medical Journal 323 (December 22–29, 2001): 1446–9.

15. R. M. Carney et al., "Change in Heart Rate and Heart Rate Variability during Treatment for Depression in Patients with Coronary Heart Disease," *Psychosomatic Medicine* 62 (2000): 639–47.

16. Laura D. Kubzansky et al., "Is the Glass Half Empty or Half Full? A Prospective Study of Optimism and Coronary Heart Disease in the Normative Aging Study," *Psychosomatic Medicine* 63 (2001): 910–6.

Chapter 12: **Connection**

1. L. G. Russek and G. E. Schwartz, "Feelings of Parental Caring Predict Health Status in Midlife: A Thirty-five-Year Follow-up to the Harvard Mastery of Stress Study," *Journal of Behavioral Medicine* 20, no. 1 (1997): 1–13.

2. C. B. Thomas and K. R. Duszynski, "Closeness to Parents and the Family Constellation in a Prospective Study of Five Disease States: Suicide, Mental Illness, Malignant Tumor, Hypertension and Coronary Artery Disease," *Johns Hopkins Medical Journal* 134 (1974): 251.

3. J. H. Medalie and U. Goldbourt, "Angina Pectoris among Ten-thousand Men II: Psychosocial and Other Risk Factors as Evidenced by a Multivariate Analysis of a Five-Year Incidence Study," *American Journal of Medicine* 60, no. 6 (1976): 910–21.

4. R. B. Williams et al., "Prognostic Importance of Social and Economic Resources among Medically Treated Patients with Angiographically Documented CAD," *Journal of the American Medical Association* 267, no. 4 (1992): 520–24.

5. T. E. Seeman and S. L. Syme, "Social Networks and CAD: A Comparison of the Structure and Function of Social Relations as Predictors of Disease," *Psychosomatic Medicine* 49, no. 4 (1987): 341–54.

6. B. Egolf et al., "Roseto, Pennsylvania – 'The Roseto Effect,'" *American Journal of Public Health* 82, no. 8 (1992): 1089–92.

7. L. Berkman and L. Breslow, *Healthy Ways of Living: The Alameda County Study* (New York: Oxford University Press, 1983).

8. D. Spiegel et al., "The Effect of Psychosocial Treatment on Survival of Patients with Metastatic Breast Cancer," *Lancet* ii (1989): 888–91.

9. F. I. Fawzi, N. W. Fawzi, and C. S. Hyun, "Malignant Melanoma: Effects of an Early Psychiatric Intervention; Coping and Affective State on Recurrence and Survival Six Years Later," *Archives of General Psychiatry* 50 (1993): 681–89.

10. R. D. Lane, E. M. Reiman, and M. M. Bradley, "Neuroanatomical Correlates of Pleasant and Unpleasant Emotion," *Neuropsychologia* 35 (1997): 1437–44. ———, "Psychosocial Intervention and the Natural History of Cancer," *Lancet* 2 (1989): 901.

11. J. S. Houses, K. R. Landis, and D. Umberson, "Social Relationships and Health," *Science* 241 (1998): 540–5.

12. J. T. Cacioppo, "Social Neuroscience: Autonomic, Neuroendocrine, and Immune Response to Stress," *Psychophysiology* 31 (1994): 113–28.

13. Nancy Frasure-Smith et al., "Social Support, Depression, and Mortality during the First Year after Myocardial Infarction," *Circulation* 101 (2000): 1919.

14. Ader, Felton, and Cohen, eds., *Psychoneuroimmunology* (San Diego: Academic Press, 1990).

15. J. Kiecolt-Glaser and R. Glaser, *Mind-Body Medicine* (New York: Consumer Reports Books, 1993).

16. S. Cohen, W. J. Doyle, and D. P. Skoner, "Social Ties and the Susceptibility to the Common Cold," *Journal of the American Medical Association* 277 (1997): 1940–4.

17. D. C. McClelland and C. Kershnit, "The Effect of Motivational Arousal through Films on Salivary Immunoglobin," *Psychology and Health* 2 (1988): 31–52.

18. D. Childre and H. Martin, *The HeartMath Solution* (San Francisco: HarperSanFrancisco (1999).

19. J. A. Armour and J. Ardell, *Neurocardiology* (New York: Oxford Press, 2005).

20. T. J. Lessmeier et al., "Unrecognized paroxysmal supraventricular tachycardia. Potential for misdiagnosis as panic disorder", *Archives of Internal Medicine* 157 (1997): 537–43.

21. B. Barrios-Choplin, R. McCraty, and B. Cryer, "An Inner Quality Approach to Reducing Stress and Improving Physical and Emotional Wellbeing at Work" *Stress Medicine* 13 (1997): 193–201.

22. R. McCraty et al., "The Impact of a New Emotional Self-Management Program on Stress, Emotions, Heart Rate Variability, DHEA and Cortisol", *Integrative Physiological and Behavioral Science* 33, no. 2 (April 1998): 151–70.

23. R. McCraty, M. Atkinson, L Lipsenthal, "Emotional Self-Regulation Program Enhances Psychological Health and Quality of Life in Patients with Diabetes", HeartMath Research Center, Institute of HeartMath, Publication No. 00-006. Boulder Creek, CA, 2000.

24. L. Russek and G. E. Schwartz, "Energy Cardiology", *Subtle Energies,* 5, no. 3 (1994): 195–208.

Chapter 13: **Connection and Communication**

1. Stewart et al., "Evidence on patient-doctor communication" ,*Cancer Prevention Control*, 3, no. 1 (February 1999): 25–30.

2. Kaplan et al., "Characteristics of Physicians with Participatory Decision-Making Styles", *Annals of Internal Medicine* 124, no. 5 (March 1, 1996)): 497-504.

3. Ruth Freeman, "A Psychodynamic Understanding of the Dentist-Patient Interaction," *British Dental Journal* 186, no. 10 (May 22, 1999). 503-507</>

Chapter 14: **Meditation**

1. Shauna L. Shapiro, Gary E. Schwartz, and Ginny Bonner, "Effects of Mindfulness-Based Stress Reduction on Medical and Premedical Students," *Journal of Behavioral Medicine* 21, no. 6 (December 1998): 581–99.

2. S. Rosenzweig et al., "Mindfulness-Based Stress Reduction Lowers Psychological Distress in Medical Students," *Teach Learn Medicine* 15, no. 2 (Spring 2003): 88–92.

3. S. L. Shapiro, D. E. Shapiro, and G. E. Schwartz, "Stress Management in Medical Education: A Review of the Literature," *Academic Medicine* 75, no. 7 (July 2000): 748–59.

4. Cheri Huber, *How You Do Anything Is How You Do Everything*, (Murphys, Calaifornia; Keep It Simple Books, 1988).

5. R. Vyas, and N. Dikshit, "Effect of Meditation on Respiratory System, Cardiovascular System, and Lipid Profile," *Indian Journal of Physiological Pharmacology* 46, no. 4 (October 2002): 487–91.

6. R. H. Schneider et al., "A Randomized Controlled Trial of Stress Reduction for Hypertension in Older African Americans," *Hypertension* 26, no. 5 (November 1995): 820–7.

7. R. R. Michaels et al., "Renin, Cortisol, and Aldosterone during Transcendental Meditation," *Psychosomatic Medicine* 41, no. 1 (February 1979): 50–4.

8. V. A. Barnes et al., "Acute Effects of Transcendental Meditation on Hemodynamic Functioning in Middle-Aged Adults," *Psychosomatic Medicine* 61, no. 4 (July–August 1999): 525–31.

9. J. A. Blumenthal et al., "Stress Management and Exercise Training in Cardiac Patients with Myocardial Ischemia: Effects on Prognosis and Evaluation of Mechanisms," *Archives of Internal Medicine* 157 (October 27, 1997): 2213–23.

10. A. Castillo-Richmond et al., "Effects of Stress Reduction on Carotid Atherosclerosis in Hypertensive African Americans," *Stroke, Hypertension* 31, no. 3 (March 2000): 568–73.

11. R. J. Davidson et al., "Alterations in Brain and Immune Function Produced by Mindfulness Meditation," *Psychosomatic Medicine* 65, no. 4 (July–August 2003): 564–70.

12. R. Sudsuang, V. Chentanez, and K. Veluvan, "Effect of Buddhist Meditation on Serum Cortisol and Total Protein Levels, Blood Pressure, Pulse Rate, Lung Volume and Reaction Time," *Physiology and Behavior* 50, no. 3 (September 1991): 543–8.

13. J. J. Miller, K. Fletcher, J. Kabat-Zinn, "Three-Year Follow-up and Clinical Implications of a Mindfulness Meditation-Based Stress Reduction Intervention in the Treatment of Anxiety Disorders," *General Hospital Psychiatry* 17, no. 3 (May 1995): 192–200.

14. S. L. Shapiro et al., "The Efficacy of Mindfulness-Based Stress Reduction in the Treatment of Sleep Disturbance in Women with Breast Cancer: An Exploratory Study," *Journal of Psychosomatic Research* 54, no. 1 (January 2003): 85–91.

15. L. E. Carlson et al., "Mindfulness-Based Stress Reduction in Relation to Quality of Life, Mood, Symptoms of Stress, and Immune Parameters in Breast and Prostate Cancer Outpatients," *Psychosomatic Medicine* 65, no. 4 (July–August 2003): 571–81.

16. L. E. Carlson et al., "The Effects of a Mindfulness Meditation-Based Stress Reduction Program on Mood and Symptoms of Stress in Cancer Outpatients: Six-Month Follow-up," *Support Care Cancer* 9, no. 2 (March 2001): 112–23.

17. D. K. Reibel et al., "Mindfulness-Based Stress Reduction and Health-Related Quality of Life in a Heterogeneous Patient Population," *General Hospital Psychiatry* 23, no. 4 (July–August 2001): 183–92.

18. L. Keefer and E. B. Blanchard, "A One-Year Follow-up of Relaxation Response Meditation as a Treatment for Irritable Bowel Syndrome," *Behavior Research and Therapy* 40, no. 5 (May 2002): 541–6.

19. J. Kabat-Zinn, L. Lipworth, and R. Burney, "The Clinical Use of Mindfulness Meditation for the Self-Regulation of Chronic Pain," *Journal of Behavioral Medicine* 8, no. 2 (June 1985): 163–90.

20. Nischala Joy Devi, *The Healing Path of Yoga* (New York: Three Rivers Press, 2000).

Chapter 15: **Psychosynthesis**

1. Roberto Assagioli, *Psychosynthesis* (no longer in print).

2. Roberto Assagioli, *The Act of Will* (Baltimore: Penguin Books, 1973).

3. Vivian King, *Soul Play: Turning Your Daily Dramas into Divine Comedies* (Sandwich, Massachusetts: North Star Publications, August 1998).

Chapter 16: **Moving Forward**

1. Roberto Assagioli, *The Act of Will* (New York: Viking Press, 1973).

2. David L. Cooperrider, Diana L. Whitney, and Jacqueline M. Stavros, eds., *Appreciative Inquiry Handbook: The First in a Series of AI Workbooks for Leaders of Change* ([Publisher location:] Berrett-Koehler Publishers, January 2004).

Bibliography

Menninger, R., Stress: defining the personal equation , *British Medical Journal* 29, Careers section, (March 2003), p. 326:S107

R. Alder, D. Felton, and N. Cohen, eds., *Psychoneuroimmunology.* San Diego: Academic Press, 1990.

Ahern, D. K., L. Gorkin, J. L. Anderson, C. Tierney, A. Hallstrom, C. Ewart, R. J. Capone, E. Schron, D. Kornfeld, J. A. Herd, D. W. Richardson, and M. J. Folliek. "Biobehavioral Variables and Mortality or Cardiac Arrest in the Cardiac Arrhythmia Pilot Study (CAPS)." *American Journal of Cardiology* 66 (1990): 59–62.

Anda, R., D. Williamson, D. Jones, C. Macera, E. Eaker, A. Glasman, and J. Marks. "Depressed Affect, Hopelessness, and the Risk of Ischemic Heart Disease in a Cohort of U.S. Adults." *Epidemiology* 4 (1993): 285–94.

Ariyo, A. A., M. Haan, C. M. Tangen, J. C. Rutledge, M. Cushman, A. Dobs, and C. D. Furberg. "Depressive Symptoms and Risks of Coronary Heart Disease and Mortality in Elderly Americans." Cardiovascular Health Study Collaborative Research Group. *Circulation* 102, no. 15 (October 10, 2000): 1773–9.

Armour, J. A., and J. Ardell. *Neurocardiology.* New York: Oxford Press, 2005.

Arnetz, B. B. "White Collar Stress: What Studies of Physicians Can Teach Us." *Psychotherapy and Psychosomatics* 55 (1991): 197–200.

Arooma, A., R. Raitasalo, A. Reunanen, O. Impivaara, M. Heliovaara, P. Knekt, V. Lehtinen, M. Joukamaa, and J. Maatela. "Depression and Cardiovascular Diseases." *Acta Psychiatrica Scandinavica* 377 (suppl) (1994): 77–82.

Assagioli, Roberto. *The Act of Will.* New York: Viking Press, 1973. *Psychosynthesis.* No longer in print.

Barefoot, J. and M. Schroll. "Symptoms of Depression, Acute Myocardial Infarction, and Total Mortality in a Community Sample." *Circulation* 93 (1996): 1976–80.

Barefoot, J., W. G. Dahlstrom, and R. B. Williams. "Hostility, CHD Incidence, and Total Mortality: A Twenty-five-Year Follow-up Study of 255 Physicians." *Psychosomatic Medicine* 45 (1983): 59–63.

Barefoot, J. C., M. J. Helms, and D. B. Mark. "Depression and Long-Term Mortality Risk in Patients with Coronary Artery Disease." *American Journal of Cardiology* 78 (1996): 613–7.

Barnes, V. A., F. A. Treiber, J. R. Turner, H. Davis, and W. B. Strong. "Acute Effects of Transcendental Meditation on Hemodynamic Functioning in Middle-Aged Adults." *Psychosomatic Medicine* 61, no. 4 (July–August 1999): 525–31.

Barrios-Choplin, B. "Restructuring Employees' Interpretive Styles to Reduce Tension and Burnout: One Company's Experience." *working paper* (1997).

Barrios-Choplin, B., R. McCraty, and B. Cryer. "An Inner Quality Approach to Reducing Stress and Improving Physical and Emotional Well-being at Work." *Stress Medicine* 13 (1997): 193–201.

Beasley, B., D. Kern, and K. Kolodner. "Job Turnover and Its Correlates among Residency Program Directors in Internal Medicine." *Academic Medicine* 76 (2001): 1127–35.

Berkman, F., and S. L. Syme. "Social Networks, Host Resistance, and Mortality: A Nine-Year Follow-up Study of Alameda County Residents." *American Journal of Epidemiology* 109 (1979): 186–204.

Berkman, L., and L. Breslow. *Healthy Ways of Living: The Alameda County Study.* New York: Oxford University Press, 1983.

L. Bernardi, "Heart Rate Variability Enhanced by Prayer and Mantra Recitation." British Medical Journal 323 (December 22–29, 2001): 1446–9.

Blumenthal, J. A., M. Babyak, J. Wei, C. O'Connor, R. Waugh, E. Eisenstein, D. Mark, A. Sherwood, P. S. Woodley, R. J. Irwin, and G. Reed. "Usefulness of Psychosocial Treatment of Mental Stress-Induced Myocardial Ischemia in Men." *American Journal of Cardiology* 89, no. 2 (January 15,2002): 164–8.

Blumenthal, J. A., W. Jiang, M. A. Babyak, D. S. Krantz, D. J. Frid, R. E. Coleman, R. Waugh, M. Hanson, M. Appelbaum, C. O'Connor, and J. J. Morris. "Stress Management and Exercise Training in Cardiac Patients with Myocardial Ischemia: Effects on Prognosis and Evaluation of Mechanisms." *Archives of Internal Medicine* 157 (October 27, 1997): 2213–23.

Brown, Shanaree, and Richard B. Gunderman. "Viewpoint: Enhancing the Professional Fulfillment of Physicians." Practicing Physicians. *Academic Medicine* 81, no. 6 (June 2006): 577–82.

Bruhn, J. G., A. Parades, C. A. Adsett, and S. Wolf. "Psychological Predictors of Sudden Death in Myocardial Infarction." *Journal of Psychosomatic Research* 18 (1974): 187–91.

Buchbinder, S., M. Wilson, C. Melick, and N. Powe. "Primary Care Physician Job Satisfaction and Turnover." *American Journal of Managed Care* 7 (2001): 702–13.

Buchbinder SB, Wilson M, Melick CF, Powe NR.. "Estimates of Costs of Primary Care Physician Turnover." *American Journal of Managed Care* 5 (1999): 1431–38.

Burns, David. *The Feeling Good Handbook*. New York: Plume, 1990.

Bush, D. E., R. C. Ziegelstein, M. Tayback, D. Richter, S. Stevens, H. Zahalsky, and J. A. Fauerbach. "Even Minimal Symptoms of Depression Increase Mortality Risk after Acute Myocardial Infarction." *American Journal of Cardiology* 88, no. 4 (August 15, 2001): 337–41.

Cacioppo, J. T. "Social Neuroscience: Autonomic, Neuroendocrine, and Immune Response to Stress." *Psychophysiology* 31 (1994): 113–28.

Carlson, L. E., M. Speca, K. D. Patel, and E. Goodey. "Mindfulness-Based Stress Reduction in Relation to Quality of Life, Mood, Symptoms of Stress, and Immune Parameters in Breast and Prostate Cancer Outpatients." *Psychosomatic Medicine* 65, no. 4 (July–August 2003): 571–81.

Carlson, L. E., Z. Ursuliak, E. Goodey, M. Angen, and M. Speca. "The Effects of a Mindfulness Meditation-Based Stress Reduction Program on Mood and Symptoms of Stress in Cancer Outpatients: Six-Month Follow-up." *Support Care Cancer* 9, no. 2 (March 2001): 112–23.

Carney, R.M., K. E. Freedland, P. K. Stein, J. A. Skala, P. Hoffman, and A. S. Jaffe, "Change in Heart Rate and Heart Rate Variability during Treatment for Depression in Patients with Coronary Heart Disease." *Psychosomatic Medicine* 62 (2000): 639–47.

Carney, R. M., M. W. Rich, K. E. Freedland, J. Saini, A. teVelde, C. Simeone, and K. Clark. "Major Depressive Disorder Predicts Cardiac Events in Patients with Coronary Artery Disease." *Psychosomatic Medicine* 50 (1988): 627–33.

Carney, Robert M., James A. Blumenthal, Phyllis K. Stein, Lana Watkins, Diane Catellier, Lisa F. Berkman, Susan M. Czajkowski, Christopher O'Connor, Peter H. Stone, and Kenneth E. Freedland. "Depression, Heart Rate Variability, and Acute Myocardial Infarction." *Circulation* 104 (2001): 2024.

Castillo-Richmond, A., R. H. Schneider, C. N. Alexander, R. Cook, H. Myers, S. Nidich, C. Haney, M. Rainforth, and J. Salerno. "Effects of Stress Reduction on Carotid Atherosclerosis in Hypertensive African Americans." *Stroke. Hypertension* 31, no. 3 (March 2000): 568–73.

Center C, Davis M, Detre T, Ford DE, Hansbrough W, Hendin H, Laszlo J, Litts DA, Mann J, Mansky PA, Michels R, Miles SH, Proujansky R, Reynolds CF 3rd, Silverman MM. "Confronting Depression and Suicide in Physicians: A Consensus Statement." *Journal of the American Medical Association* 289 (2003): 3161–6.

Childre, D., and H. Martin. *The HeartMath Solution*. San Francisco: HarperSanFrancisco, 1999.

Cohen, S., W. J. Doyle, and D. P. Skoner. "Social Ties and the Susceptibility to the Common Cold." *Journal of the American Medical Association* 277 (1997): 1940–4.

Cooperrider, David L., Diana L. Whitney, and Jacqueline M. Stavros, eds. *Appreciative Inquiry Handbook: The First in a Series of AI Workbooks for Leaders of Change.* [Publisher location:] Berrett-Koehler Publishers, January 2004.

Davidson, R. J., J. Kabat-Zinn, J. Schumacher, M. Rosenkranz, D. Muller, S. F. Santorelli, F. Urbanowski, A. Harrington, K. Bonus, and J. F. Sheridan. "Alterations in Brain and Immune Function Produced by Mindfulness Meditation." *Psychosomatic Medicine* 65, no. 4 (July–August 2003): 564–70.

Delnevo, C. D., D. J. Abatemarco, and A. R. Gotsch. "Health Behaviors and Health Promotion: Disease Prevention Perceptions of Medical Students." *American Journal of Preventive Medicine* 12 (1996): 38–43.

Denoillet, J. and D. L. Brutsaert. "Personality, Disease Severity, and the Risk of Long-Term Cardiac Events in Patients with a Decreased Ejection Fraction after Myocardial Infarction." *Circulation* 97 (1998): 167–73.

Devi, Nischala Joy. *The Healing Path of Yoga*. New York: Three Rivers Press, 2000.

Egolf, B., J. Lasker, S. Wolf, and L. Potvin. "Roseto, Pennsylvania — The Roseto Effect." *American Journal of Public Health* 82, no. 8 (1992): 1089–92.

Ellis, Albert. *A New Guide to Rational Living*. Los Angeles: Wilshire Book Company, 1961.

Everson, S. A., D. E. Goldberg, G. A. Kaplan, R. D. Cohen, E. Pukkala, J. Tuomilehto, and J. Salonen. "Hopelessness and Risk of Mortality and Incidence of Myocardial Infarction and Cancer." *Psychosomatic Medicine* 58 (1996): 113–21.

Fawzi, F. I., N. W. Fawzi, and C. S. Hyun. "Malignant Melanoma: Effects of an Early Psychiatric Intervention; Coping and Affective State on Recurrence and Survival Six Years Later." *Archives of General Psychiatry* 50 (1993): 681–9.

Firth-Cozens, J. "The Psychological Problems of Doctors." In J. Firth-Cozens and R. Payne, eds. *Stress in Health Professionals: Psychological and Organizational Causes and Interventions.* London: Wiley, 1999.

Ford, D. E., L. A. Mead, P. F. Chang, L. Cooper-Patrick, N. Wang, and M. J. Klag. "Depression Is a Risk Factor for Coronary Artery Disease in Men." *Archives of Internal Medicine* 158 (1998): 1422–6.

Frank, E., McMurray J. E.; Linzer M.; Elon L . "Career Satisfaction of U.S. Women Physicians: Results from the Women Physicians' Health Study." *Archives of Internal Medicine* 159 (July 12, 1999): 13.

Frank, Erica, Jennifer S. Carrera, Terry Stratton, Janet Bickel, and Lois Margaret Nora. "Experiences of Belittlement and Harassment and Their Correlates among Medical Students in the United States: Longitudinal Survey." *British Medical Journal* (September 6, 2006)

Frank, Erica, Holly Biola, and Carol A. Burnett. "Mortality Rates and Causes among U.S. Physicians." *American Journal of Preventive Medicine* 19, no. 3 (October 2000): 155–65.

Fraser, Robert, Mary C. Ingram, Niall H. Anderson, Caroline Morrison, Eleanor Davies, and John M. C. Connell. "Cortisol Effects on Body Mass, Blood Pressure, and Cholesterol in the General Population." *Hypertension* 33 (1999): 1364–8.

Frasure-Smith, N., F. Lesperance, and M. Talajic. "Depression and Eighteen-Month Prognosis after Myocardial Infarction." *Circulation* 91 (1995): 999–1005.

Frasure-Smith, N., F. Lesperance, M. Juneau, M. Talajic, and M. G. Bourassa. "Gender, Depression, and One-Year Prognosis after Myocardial Infarction." *Psychosomatic Medicine* 61 (1999): 26–37.

Frasure-Smith, Nancy, François Lespérance, Ginette Gravel, Aline Masson, Martin Juneau, Mario Talajic, and Martial G. Bourassa. "Social Support, Depression, and Mortality during the First Year after Myocardial Infarction." *Circulation* 101 (2000): 1919.

Freeman, Ruth. "A Psychodynamic Understanding of the Dentist-Patient Interaction." *British Dental Journal* 186, no. 10 (May 22, 1999). 503-507

Friedman, M., and R. H. Rosenman. "Association of Specific Overt Behavior Pattern with Blood and Cardiovascular Findings: Blood Cholesterol Level, Blood Clotting Time, Incidence of Arcus Senilis, and Clinical Coronary Artery Disease." *Journal of the American Medical Association* 169 (1959): 1286–96.

Fyfe, Alistair I., L. S. Rothenberg, J. D. Frederick, C. DeBeer, Rita M. Cantor, Jerome I. Rotter, Aldons J. Lusis. "Association between Serum Amyloid A Proteins and Coronary Artery Disease: Evidence from Two Distinct Arteriosclerotic Processes." *Circulation* 96 (1997): 2914–9.

Gautam, Mamta. "Women in Medicine: Stresses and Solutions." *Western Journal of Medicine* 174 (2001): 37–41.

R. Goetzel; et al.; The Health Enhancement Research Organization (HERO) Research Committee; "The Relationship Between Modifiable Health Risks and Health Care Expenditures: An Analysis of the Multi-Employer HERO Health Risk and Cost Database." Journal of Occupational and Environmental Medicine 40, no. 10 (October 1998): 1–12.

Grembowski, D., D. Paschane, P. Diehr, W. Katon, D. Martin, and D. Patrick. "Managed Care, Physician Job Satisfaction, and the Quality of Primary Care." *Journal of General Internal Medicine* 20 (2005): 271–7.

Haas, J., E. Cook, A. Puopolo, H. Burstin, P. Cleary, and T. Brennan. "Is the Professional Satisfaction of General Internists Associated with Patient Satisfaction?" *Journal of General Internal Medicine* 15 (2000): 122–8.

Heim E. "Job Stressors and Coping in Health Professions." *Psychotherapy and Psychosomatics* 55 (1991): 90–9.

Hermann, C., S. Brand-Driehorst, B. Kaminsky, E. Leibinge, H. Staats, and U. Ruger. "Diagnosis Groups and Depressed Mood as Predictors of Twenty-two-Month Mortality in Medical Patients." *Psychosomatic Medicine* 60 (1998): 570–7.

Herzberg, F. "One More Time: How Do You Motivate Employees?" *Harvard Business Review* 81 (2003): 87–96.

House, J. S., C. Robbins, and H. L. Metzner. "The Association of Social Relationships and Activities with Mortality: Prospective Evidence from the Tecumseh Community Health Study." *American Journal of Epidemiology* 116 (1982): 123–40.

Houses, J. S., K. R. Landis, and D. Umberson. "Social Relationships and Health." *Science* 241 (1998): 540–5.

Huber, Cheri. *How You Do Anything Is How You Do Everything*. Murphys, CA: Keep It Simple Books, 1988.

Kabat-Zinn, J., L. Lipworth, and R. Burney. "The Clinical Use of Mindfulness Meditation for the Self-Regulation of Chronic Pain." *Journal of Behavioral Medicine* 8, no. 2 (June 1985): 163–90.

Kaplan, S.; S. Greenfield; B. Gandek; W. H. Rogers; and J. E. Ware Jr.,"Characteristics of Physicians with Participatory Decision-Making Styles", *Annals of Internal Medicine* 124, no. 5 (March 1, 1996): 497-504..

Kaplan, G. A., J. T. Salonen, R. D. Cohen, R. J. Brand, S. L. Syme, and P. Puska. "Social Connections and Mortality from All Causes and from Cardiovascular Disease: Prospective Evidence from Eastern Finland." *American Journal of Epidemiology* 128 (1988): 370–80.

Kaplan, G. A., T. W. Wilson, R. D. Cohen, J. Kauhanen, M. Wu, and J. T. Salonen. "Social Functioning and Overall Mortality: Prospective Evidence from the Kuopio Ischemic Heart Disease Risk Factor Study." *Epidemiology* 5 (1994): 495–500.

Kawachi, I., D. Sparrow, P. S. Vokonas, and S. T. Weiss. "Decreased Heart Rate Variability in Men with Phobic Anxiety (Data from the Normative Aging Study)." *American Journal of Cardiology* 75 (1995): 882–5.

Keefer, L., and E. B. Blanchard. "A One-Year Follow-up of Relaxation Response Meditation as a Treatment for Irritable Bowel Syndrome." *Behavior Research and Therapy* 40, no. 5 (May 2002): 541–6.

Khaykin Y, Dorian P, Baker B, Shapiro C, Sandor P, Mironov D, Irvine J, Newman D. "Autonomic Correlates of Antidepressant Treatment using Heart Rate Variability Analysis." *Canadian Journal of Psychiatry* 43 (1998): 183–6.

Kiecolt-Glaser, J., and R. Glaser. *Mind-Body Medicine*. New York: Consumer Reports Books, 1993.

King, Vivian. *Soul Play: Turning Your Daily Dramas into Divine Comedies*. Sandwich, Massachusetts: North Star Publications, August 1998.

Kubzansky, Laura D., David Sparrow, Pantel Vokonas, and Ichiro Kawachi. "Is the Glass Half Empty or Half Full? A Prospective Study of Optimism and Coronary Heart Disease in the Normative Aging Study." *Psychosomatic Medicine* 63 (2001): 910–6.

Laghrissi-Thode, F., W. R. Wagner, B. G. Pollock, P. C. Johnson, and M. S. Finkel. "Elevated Platelet Factor 4 and Beta-Thromboglobulin Plasma Levels in Depressed Patients with Ischemic Heart Disease." *Biological Psychiatry* 42 (1997): 290–5.

Lane, R. D., E. M. Reiman, and M. M. Bradley. "Neuroanatomical Correlates of Pleasant and Unpleasant Emotion." *Neuropsychologia* 35 (1997): 1437–44.

"Psychosocial Intervention and the Natural History of Cancer." *Lancet* 2 (1989): 901.

Lepnurm, R., R. Dobson, A. Backman, and D. Keegan. "Factors Explaining Career Satisfaction among Psychiatrists and Surgeons in Canada." *Canadian Journal of Psychiatry* 51:(March 2006):243–255.

Lespérance, François, Nancy Frasure-Smith, Mario Talajic, and Martial G. Bourassa. "Five-Year Risk of Cardiac Mortality in Relation to Initial Severity and One-Year Changes in Depression Symptoms after Myocardial Infarction," *Circulation* Mar 2002; 105: 1049 - 1053

Lessmeier, T. J., D. Gamperling, V. Johnson-Liddon, B. S. Fromm, R. T. Steinman, M. D. Meissner and M. H. Lehmann. "Unrecognized paroxysmal supraventricular tachycardia. Potential for misdiagnosis as panic disorder", *Archives of Internal Medicine* 157 (1997): 537–43. *Archives of Internal Medicine* 157 (1997): 537–43.

Linzer, M., M. Gerrity, J. Douglas, J. McMurray, E. Williams, and T. Konrad. "Physician Job Stress: Results from the Physician Work-Life Survey." *Stress and Health* 18 (2002): 37–42.

Luskin, F., M. Reitz, K. Newell, T. G. Quinn, and W. Haskell. "A Controlled Pilot of Stress Management Training of Elderly Patients with Congestive Heart Failure." submitted for publication in *Preventive Cardiology* 2002;5(4):168-172, 176

McClelland, D. C., and C. Kershnit. "The Effect of Motivational Arousal through Films on Salivary Immunoglobin." *Psychology and Health* 2 (1988): 31–52.

McCraty, R., M. Atkinson, and L. Lipsenthal. "Emotional Self-Regulation Program Enhances Psychological Health and Quality of Life in Patients with Diabetes", HeartMath Research Center, Institute of HeartMath, Publication No. 00-006. Boulder Creek, CA, 2000.

McCraty, R., M. Atkinson, W. A. Tiller, G. Rein, and A. Watkins. "The Effects of Emotions on Short-Term Heart Rate Variability using Power Spectrum Analysis." *American Journal of Cardiology* 76 (1995): 1089.

McCraty, R., B. Barrios-Choplin, D. Rozman, M. Atkinson, and A. Watkins. "The Impact of a New Emotional Self-Management Program on Stress, Emotions, Heart Rate Variability, DHEA, and Cortisol." *Integrative Physiological and Behavioral Science* 33, no. 2 (1998): 151–70.

McCraty, Rollin, Dana Tomasino, Mike Atkinson, and Joseph Sundram. "Impact of the HeartMath Self-Management Skills Program on Physiological and Psychological Stress in Police Officers." HeartMath Research Center, publication no. 99-075. Boulder Creek: Institute of HeartMath, 1999.

McMurray, J. E., M. Linzer, T. R. Konrad, J. Douglas, R. Shugerman, and K. Nelson. "The Work Lives of Women Physicians: Results from the Physician Work-life Study." The SGIM Career Satisfaction Study Group. *Journal of General Internal Medicine* 6 (June 15, 2000): 372–80.

Medalie, J. H., and U. Goldbourt. "Angina Pectoris among Ten-thousand Men II: Psychosocial and Other Risk Factors as Evidenced by a Multivariate Analysis of a Five-Year Incidence Study." *American Journal of Medicine* 60, no. 6 (1976): 910–21.

Medstat Group and J. D. Power and Associates survey; Medstat.COM (1998).

Michaels, R. R., J. Parra, D. S. McCann, A. J. Vander. "Renin, Cortisol, and Aldosterone during Transcendental Meditation." *Psychosomatic Medicine* 41, no. 1 (February 1979): 50–4.

Miller, J. J., K. Fletcher, and J. Kabat-Zinn. "Three-Year Follow-up and Clinical Implications of a Mindfulness Meditation-Based Stress Reduction Intervention in the Treatment of Anxiety Disorders." *General Hospital Psychiatry* 17, no. 3 (May 1995): 192–200.

Miller, M. A. and R. H. Rahe. "Life Changes Scaling for the 1990s." *Journal of Psychosomatic Research* 43, no. 3 (September 1997): 279–92.

Musselman, D. L., A. Tomer, A. K. Manatunga, B. T. Knight, M. R. Porter, S. Kasey, U. Marzec, L. A. Harker, and C. B. Nemeroff. "Exaggerated Platelet Reactivity in Major Depression." *American Journal of Psychiatry* 153 (1996):1313–7.

Nemeroff, C. B., E. Widerlov, G. Bissette, H. Walleus, I. Karisson, K. Eklund, C. D. Kitts, P. T. Loosen, and W. Vale. "Elevated Concentrations of CSF Corticotropin Releasing Factor-like Immunoreactivity in Depressed Patients." *Science* 226 (1984): 1342–4.

Nonnemaker, L. "Women Physicians in Academic Medicine. *New England Journal of Medicine* 342 (2000): 399–405.

Orth-Gomer, K., and J. V. Johnson. "Social Network Interaction and Mortality: A Six-Year Follow-up Study of a Random Sample of the Swedish Population." *Journal of Chronic Disease* 40 (1987): 949–57.

Orth-Gomer, K., A. Rosengren, and L. Wilhelmsen. "Lack of Social Support and Incidence of Coronary Heart Disease in Middle-Aged Swedish Men." *Psychosomatic Medicine* 55 (1993): 37–43.
Reed, D., D. McGee, K. Yano, M. Feinleib. "Social Networks and Coronary Heart Disease among Japanese Men in Hawaii." *American Journal of Epidemiology* 117 (1983): 384–96.

Reibel, D. K., J. M. Greeson, G. C. Brainard, and S. Rosenzweig. "Mindfulness-Based Stress Reduction and Health-Related Quality of Life in a Heterogeneous Patient Population." *General Hospital Psychiatry* 23, no. 4 (July–August 2001): 183–92.

Rein, G., M. Atkinson, and R. McCraty. "The Physiological and Psychological Effects of Compassion and Anger." *Journal of Advancement in Medicine* 8, no. 2 (1995): 87.

Rosenzweig, S., D. K. Reibel, J. M. Greeson, G. C. Brainard, and M. Hojat. "Mindfulness-Based Stress Reduction Lowers Psychological Distress in Medical Students." *Teach Learn Medicine* 15, no. 2 (Spring 2003): 88–92.

Rozanski, Alan, James A. Blumenthal, and Jay Kaplan. "Impact of Psychological Factors on the Pathogenesis of Cardiovascular Disease and Implications for Therapy." *Circulation* 99 (1999): 2192–217.

Rozman, D., R. Whitaker, T. Beckman, and D. Jones. "A Pilot Intervention Program which Reduces Psychological Symptomatology in Individuals with Human Immunodeficiency Virus." *Complementary Therapies in Medicine* 4 (1996): 226.

Russek, L., and G. E. Schwartz. "Energy Cardiology, *Subtle Energies*. [*Name of Journal*] 5, no. 3 (1994): 195–208.

Russek, L. G., and G. E. Schwartz. "Feelings of Parental Caring Predict Health Status in Midlife: A Thirty-five-Year Follow-up to the Harvard Mastery of Stress Study." *Journal of Behavioral Medicine* 20, no. 1 (1997): 1–13.

Schneider, R. H., F. Staggers, C. N. Alexander, W. Sheppard, M. Rainforth, K. Kondwani, S. Smith, and C. G. King. "A Randomized Controlled Trial of Stress Reduction for Hypertension in Older African Americans." *Hypertension* 26, no. 5 (November 1995): 820–7.

Schoenbach, V. J., B. H. Kaplan, L. Fredman, and D. G. Kleinbaum. "Social Ties and Mortality in Evans County, Georgia." *American Journal of Epidemiology* 123 (1986): 577–91.

Seeman, T. E., G. A. Kaplan, L. Knudsen, R. Cohen, and J. Guralnik. "Social Network Ties and Morality among the Elderly in the Alameda County Study." *American Journal of Epidemiology* 126 (1987): 714–23.

Seeman, T. E., and S. L. Syme. "Social Networks and CAD: A Comparison of the Structure and Function of Social Relations as Predictors of Disease." *Psychosomatic Medicine* 49, no. 4 (1987): 341–54.

Shapiro, S. L., R. R. Bootzin, A. J. Figueredo, A. M. Lopez, and G. E. Schwartz. "The Efficacy of Mindfulness-Based Stress Reduction in the Treatment of Sleep Disturbance in Women with Breast Cancer: An Exploratory Study." *Journal of Psychosomatic Research* 54, no. 1 (January 2003): 85–91.

Shapiro, S. L., D. E. Shapiro, and G. E. Schwartz. "Stress Management in Medical Education: A Review of the Literature." *Academic Medicine* 75, no. 7 (July 2000): 748–59.

Shapiro, Shauna L., Gary E. Schwartz, and Ginny Bonner. "Effects of Mindfulness-Based Stress Reduction on Medical and Premedical Students." *Journal of Behavioral Medicine* 21, no. 6 (December 1998): 581–99.

Spiegel, D., J. R. Bloom, H. C. Kraemer, and E. Gottheil. "The Effect of Psychosocial Treatment on Survival of Patients with Metastatic Breast Cancer." *Lancet* ii (1989): 888–91.

Stewart et al., "Evidence on patient-doctor communication" ,*Cancer Prevention Control*, 3, no. 1 (February 1999): 25–30.

Stewart, D. E., F. Ahmad, A. M. Cheung, B. Bergman, D.L. Dell. "Women Physicians and Stress." *Journal of Women's Health & Gender-Based Medicine*, March 2000, Vol. 9, No. 2 : 185 -190

Sudsuang, R., V. Chentanez, and K. Veluvan. "Effect of Buddhist Meditation on Serum Cortisol and Total Protein Levels, Blood Pressure, Pulse Rate, Lung Volume and Reaction Time." *Physiology and Behavior* 50, no. 3 (September 1991): 543–8.

Sundquist, J., and S. Johansson. "High Demand, Low Control, and Impaired General Health: Working Conditions in a Sample of Swedish General Practitioners." *Scandinavian Journal of Public Health* 28 (2000): 123–31.

Task Force of the European Society of Cardiology and the North American

Society for Pacing and Electrophysiology, *Circulation* 93 (1996): 1043–65.

Taylor, Shelley E., Laura Cousino Klein, Brian P. Lewis, Tara L. Gruenewald, Regan A. R. Gurung, John A. Updegraff. "Biobehavioral Responses to Stress in Females: Tend-and-Befriend, Not Fight-or-Flight." *Psychological Review* 107, no. 3 (July 2000): 411–29.

Thomas, C. B., and K. R. Duszynski. "Closeness to Parents and the Family Constellation in a Prospective Study of Five Disease States: Suicide, Mental Illness, Malignant Tumor, Hypertension, and Coronary Artery Disease." *Johns Hopkins Medical Journal* 134 (1974): 251.

Tiller, W., R. McCraty, and M. Atkinson. "Cardiac Coherence: A New, Noninvasive Measure of Autonomic Nervous System Order." *Alternative Therapies in Health and Medicine* 2, no. 1 (1996): 52.

Vaishnav S, Stevenson R, Marchant B, Lagi K, Ranjadayalan K, Timmis AD. "Relation between Heart Rate Variability Early after Acute Myocardial Infarction and Long-term Mortality." *American Journal of Cardiology* 73 (1994): 653–7.

Veith, R. C., N. Lewis, O. A. Linares, R. F. Barnes, M. A. Raskind, E. C. Villacres, M. M. Murburg, E. A. Ashleigh, S. Castillo, E. R. Peskind. "Sympathetic Nervous System Activity in Major Depression: Basal and Desipramine-Induced Alterations in Plasma Norepinephrine Kinetics." *Archives of General Psychiatry* 51, no. 5 (May 1994): 411–22.

Vogt, T., J. P. Mullooly, D. Ernst, C. R. Pope, and J. F. Hollis. "Social Networks as Predictors of Ischemic Heart Disease, Cancer, Stroke and Hypertension: Incidence, Survival, and Mortality." *Journal of Clinical Epidemiology* 45 (1992): 659–66.

Vogt, T., C. Pope, J. Mullooly, and J. Hollis. "Mental Health Status as a Predictor of Morbidity and Mortality: A Fifteen-Year Follow-up of Members of a Health Maintenance Organization." *American Journal of Public Health* 84 (1994): 227–31.

von Känel, Roland, Paul J. Mills, Claudia Fainman, and Joel E. Dimsdale. "Effects of Psychological Stress and Psychiatric Disorders on Blood Coagulation and Fibrinolysis: A Biobehavioral Pathway to Coronary Artery Disease?" *Psychosomatic Medicine* 63 (2001): 531–44.

Vyas, R., and N. Dikshit. "Effect of Meditation on Respiratory System, Cardiovascular System, and Lipid Profile." *Indian Journal of Physiological Pharmacology* 46, no. 4 (October 2002): 487–91.

Welin, L., G. Tibblin, K. Svardsudd, B. Tibblin, S. Ander-Peciva, B. Larsson, and L. Wilhelmsen. "Prospective Study of Social Influences on Mortality: The Study of Men Born in 1913 and 1923." *Lancet* 2 (1985): 915–8.

Whitworth, Judith A., George J. Mangos, and John J. Kelly. "Cushing, Cortisol, and Cardiovascular Disease." *Hypertension* 36 (2000): 912.

Williams, R.B.; J. C. Barefoot; R. M. Califf; T. L. Haney; W. B. Saunders; D. B. Pryor; M. A. Hlatky; I. C. Siegler; D. B. Mark. "Prognostic Importance of Social and Economic Resources among Medically Treated Patients with Angiographically Documented CAD." *Journal of the American Medical Association* 267, no. 4 (1992): 520–24.

Suggested Reading

Books which inspired me deeply:

A Path with Heart: A Guide through the Perils and Promises of Spiritual Life
– Jack Kornfeld
I read this book on a plane flight from San Francisco to Florida. I was a different person when I got off that plane. Jack is a psychologist and meditation teacher. This book tells of his journey towards living from his heart. Deep, sweet and inspirational.

That Which You Are Seeking Is Causing You to Seek
– Cheri Huber
I am a huge fan of all of Cheri's books. This is the one, handed to me by a patient, that captured me. It is a gentle and simple reminder to be present in life, stop whining and to learn how to enjoy the moment. I encourage you to look at all of Cheri's titles and pick the one which resonates for you. If you can't decide, start here.

What We May Be: Techniques for Psychological and Spiritual Growth through Psychosynthesis
– Piero Ferrucci
This book is filled with exercises and thoughts around the concepts of Psychosynthesis and our personality structure. It will help you to become more mindful, aware and to understand yourself more deeply.

More fun reads:

The Living Energy Universe
– Gary Schwartz and Linda Russek
Although Gary and Linda's writing style is a bit scattered and un-focused, the concepts presented here are worth consideration. Is it possible that we affect each other, just by being? What effect do we have on the universe as a whole?

Soul Play
– Vivian King, PhD
This is a fun way to look at our personalities. The basic premise is that you are the director of you life play, that your sub-personalities are the actors and that god is the playwright. You get to choose the actors you need for each part of the play, but god writes the script. This leaves you in a fun dance between creation and acceptance.

For you and your patients:

The HeartMath Solution
– Doc Lew Childre & Howard Martin
This book changed my life in a simple and fun way. Through it I learned many of the techniques which I use in my workshops. As a meditation practitioner

for many years, I knew how to calm myself and feel connected with a larger purpose, but I didn't have quick tools to get calm and clear in the moment of stressful events. This book did it for me and explained the neuro-physiology behind the techniques. It is written in lay language so you and your patient will understand it deeply.

Emotional Intelligence
– Daniel Goleman, PhD
This book explains why some people are successful and others, who are equally intelligent, are not. Success in life takes intellectual knowledge and the abiliy to interact healthfully with others. For any of you interested in being a better manager or parent, I highly recommend this one.

Dr. Dean Ornish's Program for Reversing Heart Disease
– Dean Ornish, MD
This book explains how the best way to achieve health is to live a completely balanced life. Dean explains how diet, exercise and managing stress affect the heart's health. It is backed up with solid research and great stories.

Love & Survival: 8 Pathways to Intimacy and Health
– Dean Ornish, M.D
Here Dean does a masterful job at reviewing the literature on relationships and health. Beautifully done and inspiring.

Chained to the Desk
– Bryan Robinson
This book is the best description of addictive behaviors ever written. I consider it a must read for doctors for themselves and those they work with as well as patients who have addictive or compulsive tendencies. It describes the genesis of the behaviors and the effects in can have on the family. It also describes care addiction or the need to be needed, an issue for many of us in health care.

Co-dependent No More
– Melody Beattie
While this was originally written for people managing addiction, it aptly frames the concepts of living for others which is the root cause of care fatigue. Many of us docs suffer from this indeed.

Intellectual adventures
Neurocardiology
– Ardell and Armor, editors
This is a science text book of the interactions of brain and heart. It is a detailed scientific read, very dry but very informative. Only for those who want to ponder this area deeply.

Psychosynthesis; A Collection Of Basic Writings
– Roberto Assagioli, MD
This is the book of Psychosynthesis for Psychiatric professionals. It does go in and out of print regularly. I recommend it for those of you who will be teaching patients these techniques.

The Act of Will: A Guide to Self-Actualization & Self-Realization
– Roberto Assagioli, MD
This book is also written for the health professional. It is a great description of willfulness and how to enhance it. Also in and out of print.

About the Author

Lee Lipsenthal, MD, is the founder of Finding Balance in a Medical Life. He has served as medical director of Lifestyle Advantage and HeartMath LLC and was vice president and medical director of the Preventive Medicine Research Institute, with Dr. Dean Ornish, in Sausalito, California. He has also served as the president of the American Board of Holistic Medicine. He is a board-certified internist with postgraduate training in cholesterol disorders and cardiac rehabilitation.

He received his BS from George Washington University and his MD from Howard University, both in Washington, D.C. He completed his internship and residency at the Medical College of Pennsylvania. During his residency he developed the first multidisciplinary cardiac rehabilitation program in Philadelphia.

He then went on to become director of Cardio-Vascular Services for the Benjamin Franklin Clinic in Philadelphia, as well as a staff physician at The Pennsylvania Hospital. In this role, he developed treatment programs for patients with heart disease or risk of heart disease. He developed corporate wellness programs for national companies and consulted on patients with cholesterol disorders at the hospital.

Dr. Lipsenthal spent ten years developing clinical programs and lectures in prevention and treatment of heart disease. He has traveled the world as a lecturer and consultant to hospitals, national and international medical associations, and heart associations. He has developed and implemented nationwide research projects evaluating the effect of comprehensive lifestyle modification aimed at reversing heart disease, with Dr. Dean Ornish, as well as research projects evaluating the effects of psychosocial-spiritual techniques on cardiovascular outcomes and function.

Dr. Lipsenthal works with the American Medical Association and Canadian Medical Associations in the areas of physician health, and has developed seminars for physicians to enhance their well-being. The content of these seminars focuses on the physical, mental, emotional, and spiritual health of physicians and their families. These seminars have been delivered to individual physicians and physician families as well as within large medical groups and medical training programs such as Kaiser Permanente, Sentara, Hill Physicians, Physicians Associates, St. Luke's Medical System, and University of California.

For more information on programs, materials, and lectures:
800-769-0638
www.FindingBalanceProductions.com

FINDING BALANCE IN A MEDICAL LIFE